HODDER SCIENCE

Summary Book

OUSEDALE SCHOOL

Nigel Heslop
David Brodie
James Williams

Hodder Murray

A MEMBER OF THE HODDER HEADLINE GROUP

Acknowledgements

The authors and publishers would like to thank Marguerite Hall for writing the introduction.

Every effort has been made to trace all copyright holders, but if any have been inadvertently overlooked the Publishers will be pleased to make the necessary arrangements at the first opportunity.

The Publishers would like to thank the following for permission to reproduce copyright material:

Action Plus (58 bottom left, 141, 143, 156); Alamy (7 bottom); Andrew Lambert (57 top left, 62, 72, 78, 87 all, 88 all, 90 all, 91 left, 94 all, 95 right, 122, 137 right); Associated Press (83 bottom); BBC Natural History Unit (39 top right); Bob Battersby (23 bottom, 32 top, 33 all); British Antarctic Survey (127); Bruce Coleman Limited (36, 39 left, middle and bottom right, 40 top right and bottom three, 43 both); Corbis (83 top, 85 top and bottom left, 103 bottom, 151)/Carl & Ann Purcell (162 bottom); David Brodie (145); Elizabeth Whiting (85 top right); GSF Picture Library (100, 102); Hodder & Stoughton (12 bottom, 71, 85 middle right, 113 bottom); Holt Studios (11 both, 16, 23 middle, 40 top left, 50, 51); Hulton Getty (58 top left, 85 bottom right); James Mayer (12 top); Life File Photo Library (57 middle right and bottom right, 67 top and third from bottom, 105 all, 106, 126)/ Emma Lee (22 all, 23 top, 108 top and middle, 112 bottom, 114, 137 left)/ Fraser Ralston (159)/ Nigel Sitwell (113 top); Nescafé (95 left); New Media (91 right); Nigel Heslop (56 top right, 77, 82, 96); Oxford Scientific Films (12 middle, 37, 42 both); Peter Arnold Inc./ Matt Meadows (32 middle left); Press Association (60); Ronald Grant Archive (170, 171 top); Ruth Hughes (85 middle left); Science Photo Library (14 top left, 103 top)/ Andrew Syred (2 top left, bottom left and bottom right)/ Bruce Iverson (128)/ BSIP DR LR (175 top)/ Dan Schechter (146 middle left)/ David Parker (67 third from top, 171 bottom)/ Don Fawcett (7 top)/ European Space Agency (154 bottom)/ Dr E. Walker (32 bottom)/ Eye of Science (14 bottom left)/ Dr Jeremy Burgess (14 bottom right)/ John Heseltine (35 top)/ Mark Burnett (56 top left)/ Martin Bond (67 second from top)/ Martin Dohrn (117)/ Martyn F Chillmaid (124)/ NASA (146 bottom right, 149, 162 top)/ Novosti (146 top right)/ Peter Menzel (56 bottom right)/ Robert Knowles (107)/ Secchi-Lecaque, Roussel UCLAF CNRI (2 top right)/ Schleichkorn, Custom Medical Stock Photo (32 middle right)/ Simon Fraser (35 middle and bottom)/ Takeshi Takahara (159)/ Tony Craddock (108 bottom)/ University of Dundee (154 top)/ L Willatt, East Anglian Regional Genetics Service (15)/ Dr Yorgos Nikas (14 top right); Still Pictures/ J P Vantighem (112 top)/ Mark Edwards (111); The Wellcome Trust, Medical Photographic Library (57 bottom left, 175 bottom); Weston Point Studios Limited (97)

Although every effort has been made to ensure that website addresses are correct at time of going to press, Hodder Murray cannot be held responsible for the content of any website mentioned in this book. It is sometimes possible to find a relocated web page by typing in the address of the home page for a website in the URL website window of your browser.

Orders: please contact Bookpoint Ltd, 130 Milton Park, Abingdon, Oxon OX14 4SB. Telephone: (44) 01235 827720. Fax: (44) 01235 400454. Lines are open from 9.00–6.00, Monday to Saturday, with a 24 hour message answering service. Visit our website at www.hodderheadline.co.uk.

© Nigel Heslop, David Brodie, James Williams 2004
First published in 2004 by
Hodder Murray, a member of the Hodder Headline Group 338 Euston Road
London NW1 3BH

Impression number   10 9 8 7 6 5 4 3 2
Year   2010 2009 2008 2007 2006

Cover photo from SPL
Typeset in Garamond 11.5 pt by Fakenham Photosetting Limited, Fakenham, Norfolk
Printed in Italy

A catalogue record for this title is available from the British Library

ISBN-10: 0 340 88338 3
ISBN-13: 978 0 340 88338 9

Contents

Introduction

Revision tips for SATs exams

To do well in SATs or any other test, or simply just to increase your knowledge, you must do these things with what you learn:

- **Take in the new**
  Take in the new information and try to understand it.

- **Link with the old**
  Link this new information with other things you already know.

- **Remember**
  Find ways to remember this new information and revise it.

- **Send it out**
  Express this knowledge to people when they ask questions or when taking an exam.

Everyone's brain is amazingly clever. It is cleverer than any computer but we often don't know how to use it! We don't get a manual or a 'Help' button!

Take in the new

The brain takes information in through the senses: seeing, hearing, touching, smelling and tasting.

Sometimes the information goes very quickly and dramatically from the sense to the brain – it is easy to understand.

What's that smell? BURNING!

Sometimes we need to ask more questions until we fully understand. Some people find it very much easier to understand if the information has come through hearing and listening. They can concentrate on a teacher talking. They are using their **auditory** sense.

Others need to read about it, to look at pictures or diagrams, to use their EYES not just their ears. They are using their **visual** sense.

Many other people only really understand if they try it out for themselves, by doing an experiment or making a model. They are using their **kinaesthetic** – or movement and feeling – sense.

Our brains are all very clever but they are different. It is useful to know how your brain works. Try the quiz on page vi–vii which will help you find this out.

Link with the old

When the brain receives the new bit of knowledge and makes sense of it, it can then link it with other bits of information, just like putting in new pages in the right place in your file or in a filing cabinet.

We learn that PHOTOSYNTHESIS is to do with plants making food using the light of the sun. PHOTO means LIGHT. So we can link that to other 'photo' words such as PHOTOGRAPHY – we already know that LIGHT is needed to take a photograph.

OXIDISING and OXIDATION must be to do with OXYGEN. Oxygen is in the air. So OXIDATION and OXIDISING must have something to do with AIR.

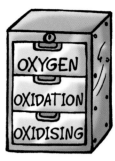

We learn that EXOTHERMIC and ENDOTHERMIC are chemical changes to do with heat energy. (*'Therm'* is to do with heat – think of *thermal* vest!). We can link this new word, **EX**OTHERMIC, with a word we already know – **EXIT** (Way Out) so exothermic must mean giving out heat.

THERMAL VEST

Remembering

So, now you have understood the information and linked the new facts with those you already know. **How do you remember it?**

First of all, you have got to *want* to!

Early humans' brains said, *'fight or flight!'* People learnt very quickly to run away from a wild animal if they wanted to live. But if they *had* to find food that day or else they would starve to death, they attacked instead!

I want food!

You need a reason to get your brain working for success in SATs (please your parents, earn a reward, feel good about yourself etc.). Keep that reason at the front of your mind. Get excited at the thought of doing well! Use the ideas on these pages to make it fun and stress free.

I want SUCCESS!

If you haven't yet done the Quiz on page vi, do it now.

Send the information out

This should be easy, if you've understood the information and remembered it! So relax, be confident and follow these simple common sense rules for success in your tests.

- Read each question twice – some questions give lots of information you have to read before you get to the part you have to answer.

- Look at the space for your answer and the marks for it. A short space and '1 mark' will probably mean just a word or two is expected. Several lines will mean more is needed.

- The words '*Explain*' and '*Describe*' in the question mean you need to make sure you really make it clear to the reader that you know. You may think that your answer is too obvious. Write it anyway.

- If you have learnt a mnemonic (silly rhyme) to help you remember something, scribble it down quickly on the page somewhere.

  If you have visualised a diagram or a list, try to picture it in your mind and then quickly draw it in rough somewhere.

  You can then look at these pieces of information calmly when answering the questions.

- If you come to a question that you don't like, leave it and do the ones you find easy first. If you know you need to add something but can't think of it, leave it and come back to it later. It is a good idea to put a mark at the question so you don't miss it when you are looking back. If you still don't know the answer, GUESS!

- Keep an eye on the clock!

Hodder Science Summary Book

Quiz

Write your answers a), b) or c) on a sheet of paper, numbered 1–13

1 You have to make a model of a house using cardboard. Do you prefer to:

a) follow the diagram and instructions

b) ask someone to tell you what to do

c) just try building it.

2 If you are very annoyed with someone, do you:

a) shout angry words

b) punch something

c) go all quiet and upset.

3 When you have to sit still in class for a long time, do you want to:

a) daydream or doodle

b) fidget or move around

c) mutter to yourself or talk to others.

4 How would you describe your schoolbag and possessions?

a) My things are organised.

b) I can never find things.

c) It looks messy but I know where things are.

5 What do you remember most about a film you have seen:

a) the actions

b) the words and the music

c) the scenery and how the people looked.

6 Is your favourite way to relax:

a) read or watch TV

b) listen to music

c) go out and be active.

7 Do you think you are good at:

a) telling jokes

b) remembering what someone looks like

c) making things.

8 You are going to learn to play a new sport. Do you:

a) get out and try to play

b) ask someone who plays for some tips

c) watch people playing first.

9 If you know you have upset your mum, do you:

a) write her a little note

b) talk to her and say you're sorry

c) go up to her and give her a hug.

10 Which of these puzzles do you like doing best:

a) 'spot the difference' picture puzzle

b) 'name that tune' music puzzle

c) putting together a wooden puzzle.

You need a friend to help you here. Your friend must look at your eyes and mark, on your answer sheet, where your eyes move when they ask you the following questions. They must mark a) up b) middle or c) down for each question.

a) **b)** **c)**

11 What did you do for your last birthday?

12 What do you do on Christmas morning?

13 Pretend you can see an elephant wearing a swimsuit. What colour is it and what else is the elephant wearing?

Finding your learning style – (quiz answers)

Visual (seeing), Auditory (hearing) or Kinaesthetic (doing)

Mark V, A or K for each answer on your sheet.

1	2	3	4
a) V	a) A	a) V	a) V
b) A	b) K	b) K	b) A
c) K	c) V	c) A	c) K

5	6	7	8
a) K	a) V	a) A	a) K
b) A	b) A	b) V	b) A
c) V	c) K	c) K	c) V

9	10	11	12
a) V	a) V	a) V	a) V
b) A	b) A	b) A	b) A
c) K	c) K	c) K	c) K

13
a) V
b) A
c) K

Now add up your scores.

More **Visual**? You learn best through looking.
More **Auditory**? Your easiest way of learning is through listening.
More **Kinaesthetic**? You learn best a practical way.

Do you find it hard to concentrate if you are trying to read and the teacher is reading it aloud at the same time? **You may be a visual or a kinaesthetic learner.**

Do you love science experiments, or technology lessons? **You may be a real hands-on person, with a very kinaesthetic style.**

Are you the sort of person who can follow what the teacher is saying even if your head is down on the desk or you are staring out of the window? **You are probably an auditory learner.**

Did you know:

- 35% of people are mainly visual learners
- 25% are mainly auditory
- 40% are mainly kinaesthetic learners.

Did you have a mixture of V, A and K? Super! You can use any of the following ideas …

Learning styles

Have you discovered your learning style yet? (Have you done the Quiz?)

Try some of the following ideas.

If your learning style is mainly **visual:**

- write lists of key points
- highlight and use colour
- draw flow charts, spider diagrams, thinklink maps, storyboards, charts

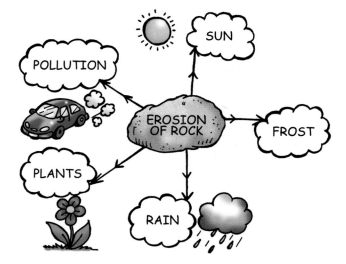

- make wall posters
- **visualise** your diagrams and pictures and lists. Close your eyes and see them in your mind. Picture what is in the top right corner, bottom left etc. **Remember: one picture is worth 1000 words!**
- think of visual tricks to remember things e.g. **A** is for **A**rtery and for **A**way (**A**rtery carries blood **A**way from the heart).

Hodder Science Summary Book

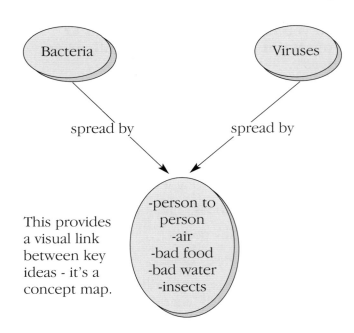

Bacteria — spread by ⟶ -person to person -air -bad food -bad water -insects ⟵ spread by — Viruses

This provides a visual link between key ideas - it's a concept map.

Distance = **S**peed x **T**ime. This is another visual aid.

If your learning style is mainly **auditory**:

- write lists of key points and read them aloud

- talk over with a friend

- teach someone else (your mum, perhaps!)

- make up silly rhymes or funny ones or even sensible ones like this: **M**y **V**ery **E**asy **M**ethod **J**ust **S**peeds **U**p **N**aming **P**lanets.

- ask someone to tape a difficult chapter for you. Listen to it when you are getting up in the morning or going to bed at night

- look at diagrams and tell the story aloud. For example 'You chew food in your mouth, you get the saliva all round it and then it passes down into the …'

- sing to your own tune e.g. 'When the bicep contracts, the tricep relaxes'.

If your learning style is mainly **kinaesthetic**:

- move around as you study

- draw and label large diagrams, then cut them up and put together again (e.g. digestive system)

- act it out – be a particle! Be a solid, liquid or gas

- get some friends together and do a role play

- make 3D models

- trace diagrams over and over

- make a flow chart or storyboard with cards and number them in order

- make a large poster and put 'Post it' stickers on as labels

- learn in a group if you can.

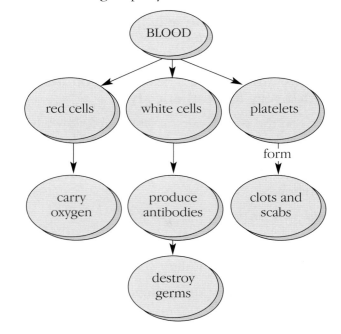

Special Treats

Everyone can use the following two SPECIALS – they are **multisensory**, because you use all your three main senses while doing them. There is lots of information going straight to the brain AT THE SAME TIME!

1　Put keywords, meanings, lists, rhymes, diagrams etc. on cards and dot them round the house. Play games with them, read them aloud, look at them carefully every time you pass!

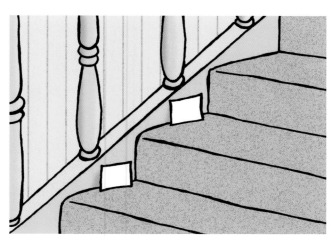

2　Listen to yourself and watch your lips move in front of a mirror as you say a fact. Try it as you say:

'Exothermic means heat going out just like exit means going out.'

Remember when you do diagrams they are for *you*. Their job is to store infomration that you can look at again later. You do not need to be an artist or to make them perfectly neat. You simply have to put the information you are trying to remember into the way your brain finds easy.

Life

1.1 Cells, tissues and organs

Cells and cell structure

Plant and animal cells have a number of things in common and a few differences. Figure 1 shows you what a typical animal cell and a typical plant cell look like.

All living tissues are made up of cells.

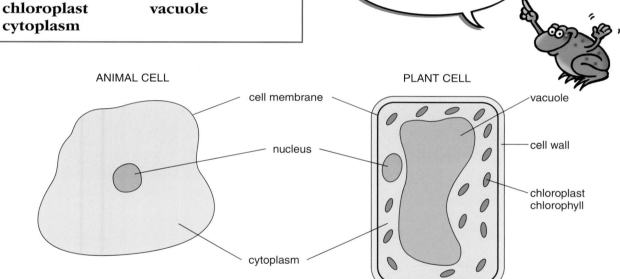

Figure 1 An animal cell and a plant cell

Cell structure	Animal cell	Plant cell	Function
cell membrane	✓	✓	Lets substances into and out of the cell.
cell wall	✗	✓	Helps to give the cell shape and support the plant.
cytoplasm	✓	✓	Chemical reactions that keep the cell alive take place here.
nucleus	✓	✓	The control centre of the cell. It contains (sets of) instructions that control both the reactions in the cytoplasm and making new cells.
large vacuole	✗	✓	This contains cell sap, a watery fluid which helps keep the cell rigid.
chloroplast	✗	✓	Contains a green chemical, chlorophyll, which uses light energy to produce sugar from water and carbon dioxide during photosynthesis.

Table 1 The difference between animal and plant cells

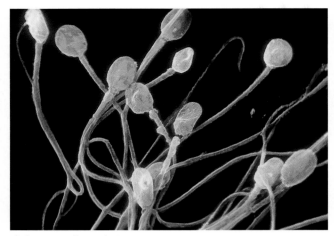

a) Sperm cells

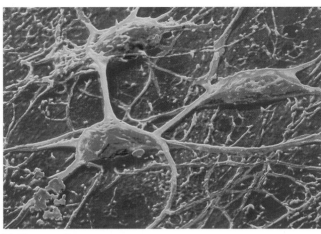

b) Nerve cells

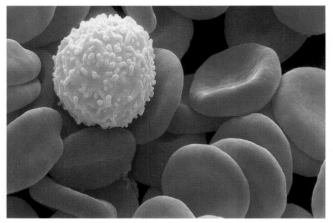

c) Red and white blood cells

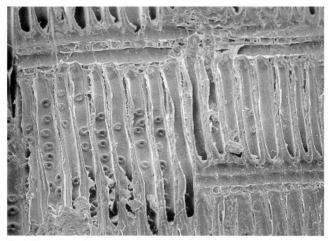

d) Xylem vessels

Figure 2 Plant and animal cells come in different shapes and sizes.

Tissues

Has aaaaanyone got a tissue?

AATISHOO!

Tissues carry out different jobs or **functions**.

A tissue is a set of similar cells working together to do a specific job.

Animal tissue	Job
skin	to protect the body and stop harmful things entering
blood	to carry oxygen, carbon dioxide and chemicals from food around the body and defend against infection
bone	to give support
nervous tissue	to carry messages
muscle	to help us move

Plant tissue	Job
xylem	to carry water and minerals from the roots to the leaves
phloem	to carry food dissolved in water around the plant

Table 2 Some examples of animal and plant tissues.

Organs and organ systems

An organ is a group of tissues. Some organs work together to make an organ system.

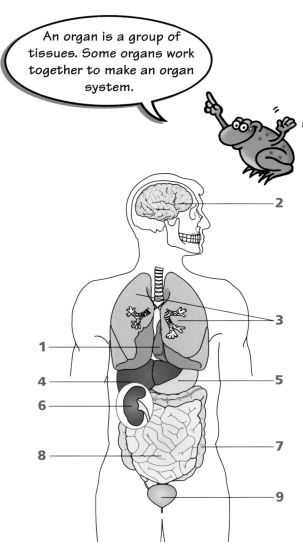

Figure 3

1 The **heart** pumps blood around the body through a network of arteries and receives blood from a network of veins. The heart is a large muscle with four chambers. Blood carries oxygen around the body and brings carbon dioxide back to the lungs. White blood cells fight off infection.

2 The **brain** is the control centre of the body. It receives information and sends out instructions to the body using a network of cells called nerves.

3 The **lungs** take air into your body from which you take oxygen. You also get rid of carbon dioxide in the air that you breathe out.

4 The **liver** acts like a filter to clean your blood. It breaks down chemicals, called toxins, that could poison you. It also stores sugar as a chemical called glycogen.

5 Food is partly broken down in the **stomach** by hydrochloric acid. Chemicals called enzymes are added to it to help break it down.

6 **Kidneys** remove waste chemicals from your blood and produce urine which can be stored in your bladder.

7 Most of the water in your food is absorbed back into your body from the **large intestine**.

8 Food is broken down in the **small intestine** to release chemicals your body can use including sugar, proteins, fats, vitamins, minerals and fibre.

9 Urine is stored in the **bladder**. It leaves the body through a thin tube called the urethra.

Humans have a number of organ systems that allow the life processes to take place.

Movement	muscle and skeletal system
Respiration	respiratory system
Sensitivity	nervous system and sense organs
Growth	digestive system
Reproduction	reproductive system
Excretion	digestive, urinary and respiratory systems
Nutrition	digestive system

Table 3 Human organ systems

Hi, if you want an easy way to remember the life processes, think of me, MRS GREN. I'll help you pass your test! The letters in my name are the first letters of each of the life processes.

Figure 4

3

Growth

As you grow and develop, the cells, tissues and organs in your body grow and change. Cells are always being replaced and old cells die and get broken down in your body.

All of the cells in your body, except mature red blood cells, have a **nucleus**. The nucleus controls what the cell does (its function) and when and how it should divide. Cells make copies of themselves when they divide.

What is cancer?

Cancer is the uncontrolled division of cells. A cancerous cell will keep on dividing and each of the cells it produces also keeps on dividing. Eventually a tumour can form. Tumours can be benign or malignant. Benign tumours are not cancer. They can usually be removed without any problem. It is the malignant tumours that are cancer. Cancerous cells can also travel around in the bloodstream and new tumours can be produced at other sites in the body. Many things can cause cancer, including exposure to radioactivity, certain chemicals and too much sunbathing.

Not all cancers will lead to death. Many cancers can be treated if caught early, either by radiotherapy (killing the cancer cells with radioactivity), chemotherapy (killing the cells with powerful drugs) or by surgery (cutting the cancerous cells out of the body).

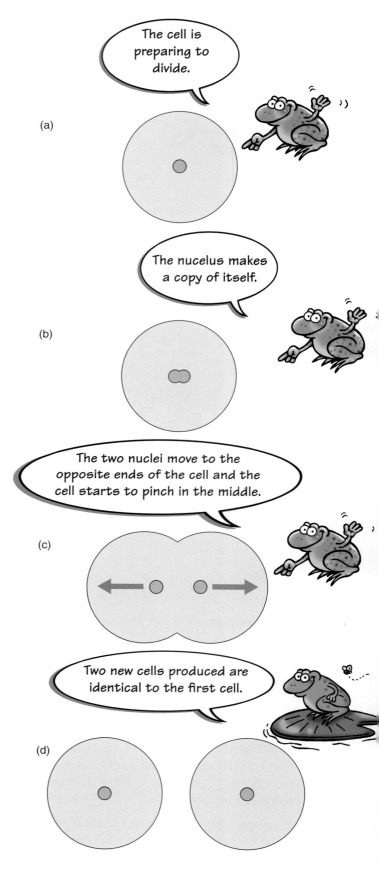

Figure 5 A cell dividing into two

Revision

Thinklinks

To help you revise and remember this work, try drawing some thinklinks maps. Use the following key words in your map.

cell   **cancer**   **tissue**   **organ growth**   **organ system**   **divide**

Prompt cards

Make a list of the key words in this section on index cards. Use a different card for each key word. Write down on the card what the word means and any other information that you think is useful. If you think it will help, copy down a simple diagram.

Questions

1 Plant cells do not have a skeleton. What do the cells have that helps them keep a definite shape?

2 Which part of a red blood cell is lost as it matures?

3 Red blood cells do not divide as they travel around our blood vessels. Why can't they divide and what could happen if they did divide as they travelled in our bloodstream?

4 Describe the sort of test that a doctor might do with a pin on a patient to find out if the patient had damaged a nerve after badly cutting themselves with a knife.

5 Explain what is meant by the term 'tumour'. What are the two main types of tumour?

6 What are the main causes of cancer that we know about?

7 How can cancer cells move around the body?

8 Draw and label a typical plant cell and a typical animal cell.

9 Explain what happens when a normal cell changes into a cancer cell.

10 There are three main methods for treating cancer. What are they?

11 For *each* method of cancer treatment, think about what the main drawbacks and advantages could be.

12 Cells divide instead of getting bigger and bigger. Draw a simple cartoon strip of an animal cell growing and dividing into two cells.

1.2 Reproduction

Key Words

egg cell	prostate gland
embryo	puberty
fertilisation	semen
foetus	scrotum
hormones	sperm cell
oestrogen	testis (testes)
ovary	umbilical cord
oviduct	vas deferens
placenta	womb
progesterone	

Male and female reproductive systems

A new life begins when a **sperm cell** from the father joins with an **egg cell** from the mother. This process is called **fertilisation**. In mammals it happens inside the female's body.

Producing sperm and egg cells

Egg cells are made inside the **ovaries**. When a girl reaches **puberty**, her ovaries start to release egg cells. In adults, one egg is released each month. In young girls the release of eggs can be irregular but it usually settles down once the girl has fully matured. This cycle is called a period, or menstruation. You can read more about it later on.

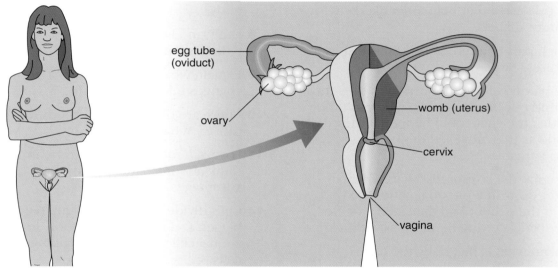

Figure 1 The female reproductive system

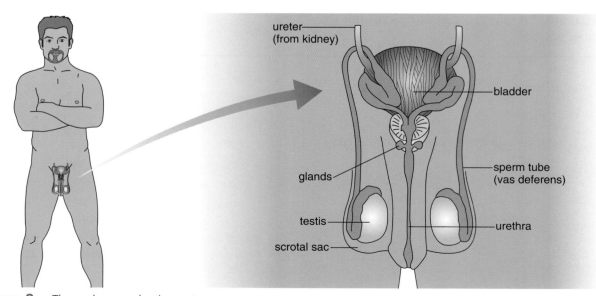

Figure 2 The male reproductive system

Internal and external fertilisation

In many animals, fertilisation takes place inside the female's body. This is not the only place where fertilisation can take place. In fish, for example, the eggs are fertilised outside the female's body. The female fish lays the eggs in water and the male fish sprays sperm over the eggs.

Sperm cells are made in the man's **testis** (the plural is **testes**). Sperm cells are very sensitive to temperature. A man's body temperature is too high for sperm cells to live and reproduce so the testis hangs outside the body in a sac of skin – the scrotal sac or **scrotum**. When sperm cells are produced, they pass through the **vas deferens**. As they pass the **prostate gland**, fluids are added which keep the sperm cells alive. The sperm and the fluid together are known as **semen**.

Fertilisation

For fertilisation to happen the sperm and egg must come into contact with each other. During sexual intercourse the man will become excited and his penis becomes stiff or erect. This happens because it fills with blood. When a woman becomes excited she produces a fluid that lubricates the vagina and the entrance to the vagina. The man's penis can be inserted into the vagina and moved in and out. Eventually the sperm are pumped into the vagina in the semen as the man ejaculates. The sperm then swim from the vagina into the womb and eventually reach the oviduct.

The egg cell passes down the **oviduct** from the ovary where it is produced. If it meets with a sperm cell and joins with it, fertilisation takes place and the egg can begin to divide. The fertilised egg will enter the **womb** where it attaches itself to the wall of the womb. It may then continue to divide and grow into a baby which will be born about nine months later.

Fertilisation is the joining together of a sperm cell and an egg cell.

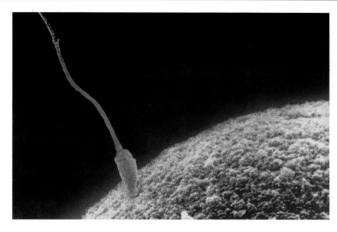

Figure 3   The egg is many times larger than the sperm. The colours have been added to make it easier to see the sperm and egg.

Figure 4   Angel fish spawning; you can see the eggs on the vegetation surface.

Growing in the womb

Once a fertilised egg settles in the wall of the womb, it begins to grow and develop into a baby. At first it is just a ball of cells which divide. After about four weeks it is possible to see the head area developing and some tiny stumps that will develop into the legs and arms.

The ball of cells is called an **embryo**. Once you can make out a head, arms, legs, etc. we call it a **foetus**.

As the baby grows in its mother's womb, it needs to be fed, have a supply of oxygen, be protected from harmful infections and get rid of waste products.

In order to do this a round disc-like organ – the **placenta** – grows on the surface of the womb. This is connected to the growing baby by a cord – the **umbilical cord**. The **amnion** is a water-filled sac that protects the foetus as it grows. The placenta is rich in blood vessels. The vessels have thin walls that allow oxygen and chemicals that the baby needs for energy and growth to pass from the mother's bloodstream into the baby's bloodstream. Any waste that the baby produces while it grows passes down the umbilical cord and across to the mother's bloodstream for the mother to get rid of. The placenta can stop some harmful substances and some bacteria from passing into the baby, but it cannot prevent everything. For example, alcohol can pass from the mother into the baby and this can harm the baby as it grows. Harmful chemicals in cigarette smoke also pass into the baby's bloodstream and can cause problems.

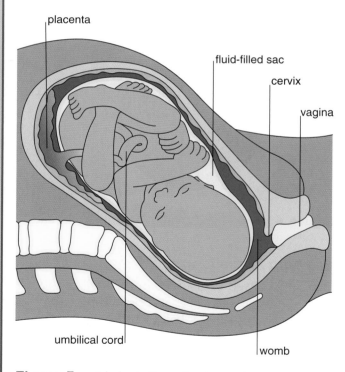

Figure 5   A baby in its mother's womb

Growing up is hard to do

Boys and girls go through a number of changes as they develop into adults. These changes happen at a stage called **puberty**.

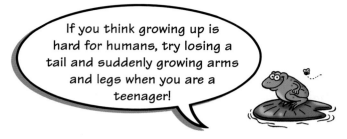

If you think growing up is hard for humans, try losing a tail and suddenly growing arms and legs when you are a teenager!

Puberty

As your body grows and matures, and you change from being a child to an adult, you go through what is called puberty.

Table 1 lists some of the changes that take place in boys and girls during puberty. Many of the changes are caused by **hormones**. Hormones are natural chemicals in your body that control things. Menstruation and growing body hair are caused by the presence of hormones.

The menstrual cycle

Once an egg is released, the womb prepares to receive it. To do this the wall of the womb thickens. The lining of the womb has a rich supply of blood vessels. If a fertilised egg does not reach the womb and attach to the lining, the body knows that the lining is not needed. It breaks down and is passed out of the body through the vagina. This process is controlled by two hormones, **progesterone** and **oestrogen**.

To begin with, periods may be irregular, but they will settle down and usually happen once every 28–30 days. The egg is released on or around day 14. The first day of bleeding in a woman is day 1 of the period.

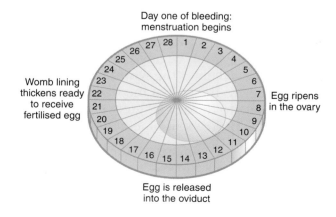

Figure 6   The menstrual cycle.

Changes at puberty	Boys	Girls
Body size	The body begins to grow faster and the shoulders broaden. More defined muscles appear.	The whole body begins to grow faster. Curves begin to appear as the body deposits fat on the hips, buttocks and thighs.
Hair	The hair on the head can become greasier. Hair grows under the arms, on the chest and legs and around the penis (pubic hair). There is an increase in the growth of facial hair.	The hair on the head can become greasier. Hair will begin to grow under the arms and around the vagina (pubic hair) and fine hair on the arms and legs can darken
Voice	The voice gets deeper and the larynx (Adam's Apple) gets larger.	The voice doesn't change much.
Skin	Mild acne or 'spots' can develop. If it gets bad a pharmacist or doctor should be seen.	Mild acne or 'spots' can develop. If it gets bad a pharmacist or doctor should be seen.
Reproductive organs	The testes grow larger and start producing sperm. The penis will grow larger and may get darker.	Breasts begin to develop (mammary glands), the ovaries start to release eggs. This triggers the start of menstruation (periods).

Table 4   Changes that take place during puberty

Revision

Copy out the tables below. Read through the chapter then see how much of the table you can complete without looking back. If you fill in the blank table in pencil, you can always rub out the pencil and use the tables again.

Name	Male or female?	What it does
oviduct		
gland		
scrotal sac		
womb (uterus)		

Changes at puberty	Boys	Girls
body size		
hair		
voice		
skin		
reproductive organs		

Questions

1 Put these in the correct order: adult, child, baby, adolescent.

2 Where are the sperm produced in the male?

3 Where are the eggs produced in the female?

4 Why are the testes outside the male body in a sac of skin?

5 What is the name for the sperm and the fluid that keeps it alive?

6 In what part of the female is sperm deposited?

7 How does the sperm get into the womb?

8 How do the eggs get to the womb?

9 What is the difference between an embryo and a foetus?

10 How does the growing foetus get a supply of oxygen and nutrients?

11 Why does the growing foetus need the mother to eat and drink sensibly and healthily during pregnancy?

12 The foetus sits inside a water-filled sac until it is ready to be born. How could this offer the foetus protection?

1.3 Variation and classification

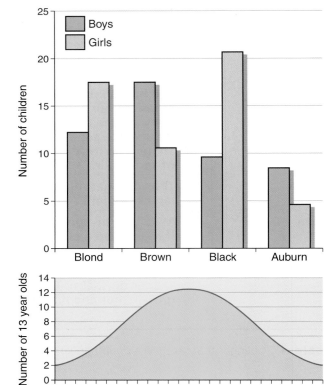

Key Words

classification	inherited
clone	range
continuous variation	selective breeding
discontinuous variation	taxonomy variation
environmental variation	

Variation

All people are different, come to that, so are all us frogs. These differences can be due to the environment or the genes we inherit from our parents.

Figure 1 a) Hair colour in 13 year old children
b) Age versus height in 13 year olds

When scientists look at the differences between living organisms, they are studying the **variation** between them. Some variations between living things are easy to see, e.g. different eye colour. Other variations will be more difficult, e.g. different blood groups.

Continuous and discontinuous variation

Scientists look at two different types of variation in living things – **continuous variation** and **discontinuous variation**.

In discontinuous variation, the variation must be one thing or another. For example, eyes are generally either blue or green or brown. Natural hair colour is usually blond or brown or black or auburn.

In continuous variation, things can have any value in a **range** of values. For example, a person's height might be anywhere between, say, 30 cm when they are born to about 2 m as an adult. People are *not* either 1 m or 1.5 m or 2 m tall!

Clones

Clones are exact copies of another individual. Scientists have found ways of artificially cloning plants and animals.

The first known **clone** of a mammal was Dolly the sheep. Dolly was created at the Roslyn Institute in Edinburgh by taking an egg from a ewe, removing the nucleus and injecting a new nucleus from a cell of a fully grown sheep. The egg then developed into an exact copy of the sheep from which the nucleus was taken.

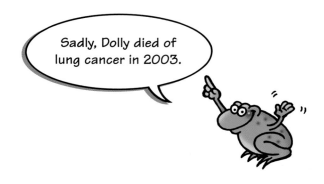

Sadly, Dolly died of lung cancer in 2003.

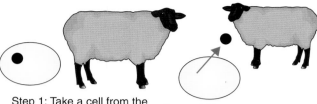

Step 1: Take a cell from the sheep you want to clone (the donor) and grow it in a petri dish with chemicals that stop the nucleus from working.

Step 2: Take an egg cell from a female sheep and take out the nucleus.

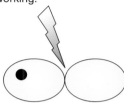

Step 3: Join the adult cell with the empty egg cell using an electric spark. The nucleus starts working again.

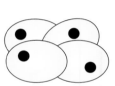 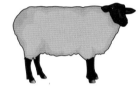

Step 4: The cell begins to grow and divide.

Step 5: The cells are transferred to the mother's womb to grow and develop as normal.

Step 6: Lambs are produced that are identical to the donor sheep.

Figure 2   How Dolly was cloned

Figure 3   The colour of the hydrangea flower depends on the type of soil.

Clones can occur naturally in the form of identical twins. Creating artificial clones is different. So far it has been very difficult to create full grown clones of animals, but clones of plants are very easy to make and occur everywhere. Plants can be cloned in a number of ways and some do it naturally.

What causes variation?

Variation in living things has different causes. Where we live and how we are brought up can cause variation, even between identical twins. If one twin overeats and happens to live in a hotter country, they would end up bigger and heavier than their twin and they may have a darker skin colour because they sunbathe a lot. This sort of variation is called **environmental variation**.

Plants and animals can also have **inherited variation** and/or environmental variation. Trees growing in windy areas tend to be thinner, mammals living in colder areas tend to have thicker coats and they are fatter, and flowers grown in different types of soil may have the flower colour determined by the type of soil.

If you look at the two photos in Figure 3 you will see that although the plants are the same, the colour of the flower is not. Pink and white hydrangeas grow in soil that is chalky (alkaline), whereas blue hydrangeas grow in soil that is acid.

Figure 4 Geoff and James are genetically identical twins but Geoff is smaller than James due to environmental factors.

Selective breeding

Scientists can breed plants and animals with particular characteristics by a process called **selective breeding**. Wheat is a very important crop. All over the world it provides food for millions of people. The wheat that we grow today, however, is very different to the wheat grown by

Figure 5 The Jacob sheep (top) is an ancient breed of sheep. Farmers used selective breeding on species similar to this to produce modern sheep species like those at the bottom.

people thousands of years ago. Originally wheat was quite a tall plant with few grains. Today, the wheat that grows in the fields is much shorter and contains a larger number of grains. This is an example of selective breeding. Some people selectively breed living things to try and improve them. By taking a fast male race-horse and a mare that is also a good race-horse, breeders can mate them with each other in the hope of producing a champion horse. In plants, breeders might use a plant that is resistant to disease to produce other varieties that are resistant to disease.

Classification

Scientists identify living organisms by using similarities and differences or variations in living things to place them into groups. This is called **classification** or **taxonomy**.

Some things can be easily grouped together, like lions and tigers, oak trees and apple trees. But for others, like a scorpion and a house spider, it is not obvious that they come from the same family.

Scientists group living things together in what are called **taxonomic groups**. There are hundreds of groups of living things.

Taxonomists divide all living things into five large groups:

Plants	**Single-celled organisms**
Animals	**Bacteria and blue green algae**
Fungi	

These large groups are called **kingdoms**. The next largest group is called **phylum**, then comes the group called **class**. This group is divided into **orders**. Then comes the **family** and finally the **genus** followed by the **species**. The species is the smallest group and contains individuals of one kind only.

My name is *Rana temporaria*, I belong to the genus Rana and all common frogs are called temporaria. My cousin *Rana esculenta* is often found in a French restaurant, but he's not dining out!

Revision

Make some revision cards for the following important facts. Use some diagrams or pictures to make the cards more interesting and visual. Remembering pictures can sometimes be easier than remembering words.

Variation

- An individual in a species can vary in many ways, e.g. size, hair colour, eye colour.
- Some characteristics are **inherited**.
- Some characteristics are caused by the environment.
- Individuals may look like their parents but are not identical to them.
- Variations may be **continuous**, e.g. height, or **discontinuous**, e.g. hair colour.
- **Selective breeding** can produce plants and animals with the best/most useful characteristics.
- Clones are offspring that are identical to their parent or another individual (e.g. an identical twin).

Classifying

- Biologists group plants and animals according to their similarities.
- The smallest group is called a **species**. In this group animals are very similar to each other and produce offspring that can also reproduce.
- Two different species may produce offspring, but these will not be able to reproduce.
- The largest group is a **kingdom**.
- There are five kingdoms: Plants, Animals, Single-celled organisms, Bacteria/blue-green algae and Fungi.

Questions

1 Classify these variables as either continuous or discontinuous variation:

   a) finger length   **d)** eye colour

   b) foot length   **e)** arm span.

   c) shoe size

2 Think of four other variables. Which would be continuous and which would be discontinuous?

3 Which of the following characteristics are inherited and which could be environmental? Which characteristics could be inherited and then affected by the way we live (environmental):

   a) weight   **g)** ability to draw

   b) hair colour   **h)** hand size

   c) height   **i)** ability to sing

   d) eye colour   **j)** skin colour

   e) nose shape   **k)** mouth shape

   f) good at maths   **l)** foot size?

4 A man with ears that stuck out had them pinned back using plastic surgery. He was convinced that this would stop any of his children having the same type of ears. Say if you think he is right or wrong and why.

5 Explain why identical twins separated at birth may not be identical if they meet up 30 years later. What may be the same about them and what might be different?

6 What advantage is there in breeding shorter varieties of wheat? (*Hint:* think about what could happen in different types of weather.)

7 Selective breeding could mean that some varieties of plants and animals become extinct. If this happens we will lose all of their characteristics, good and bad. Why do you think it is important to preserve rare plants and animals?

8 What do we mean when we say that an animal is an

   a) invertebrate?   **b)** vertebrate?

1.4 Inheritance and selection

Key Words

chromosomes
conjoined twins
DNA
fraternal twins
genes
identical twins
ovule

pollen
pollen tube
rhizome
sexual
reproduction

I inherited my good looks from my mother's side, she was Miss Pond 2003

Figure 1 Methods of sexual reproduction

Variation

Why are we all similar, but not identical?

When most cells divide the nucleus makes a copy of itself and each cell produced is identical to the cell it came from. All of the information needed to produce an identical copy of us is contained in the nucleus.

For a new life to begin, a sperm cell from the father and an egg from the mother must join together. This process is known as fertilisation. A similar thing happens in most plants. A pollen grain (the male cell) joins with an ovule (the female cell) and seeds are produced that can grow into new plants. This type of reproduction is known as **sexual reproduction**. In animals and plants it leads to new plants and animals that are similar, but not identical, to the parent.

DNA in the nucleus of the cell controls what living things look like and how they grow. In particular, they are controlled by small sections of DNA called **genes.** Every nucleus contains many thousands of genes. Genes will control the colour of your eyes and hair and many other things.

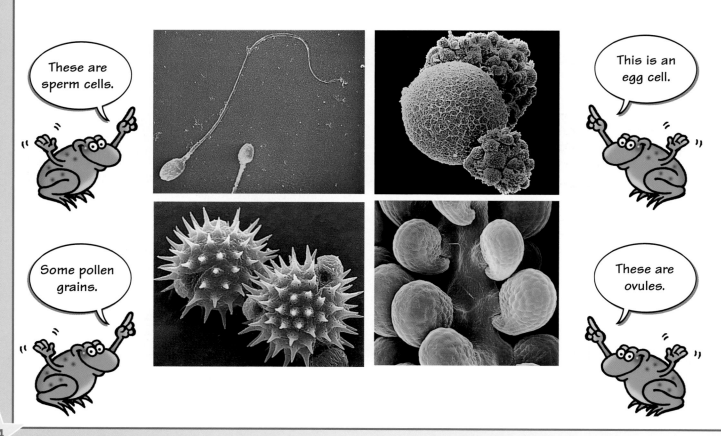

These are sperm cells.

This is an egg cell.

Some pollen grains.

These are ovules.

The genes are found on the strands of DNA called **chromosomes**. The chromosomes come in pairs. Each of our cells contains 23 pairs of chromosomes, like the ones shown in Figure 2. Egg cells and sperm cells are specialised cells, and they only have 23 single chromosomes.

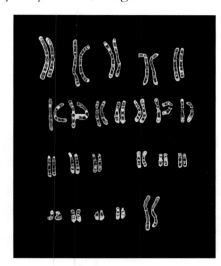

Figure 2   Human beings have 46 chromosomes in 23 pairs.

Figure 3 shows how sperm cells would be produced in an animal with only four chromosomes (two pairs).

Figure 3   Producing sex cells from an animal with only four chromosomes

When fertilisation takes place, the chromosomes pair up again. A fertilised egg in this animal would have four chromosomes, two from the father and two from the mother. There is a mixture of genes and chromosomes from the mother and father, so the offspring would have a mixture of features from the mother and father. This explains why the offspring are similar, but not identical, to the parents.

Twins

When two babies are born on the same day to the same mother, we call them **twins**. There are two types of twins – **identical** and **fraternal**.

Identical twins can be exactly the same, or there may be small differences. Just after the egg has been fertilised inside the mother, it begins to divide and grow. Before it gets too big, the embryo splits completely into two. Because the DNA in each is identical, two identical babies develop. If the embryo doesn't completely split, then **conjoined twins** can develop.

Fraternal twins happen when two *different* eggs in the mother are fertilised by two *separate* sperm. Because the DNA is not identical, the twins may be no more similar than normal siblings. They can even be of different sexes. The word fraternal actually means 'brother' but we use it to describe all twins that are not identical.

The cell divides like a normal cell, making two cells each with four chromosomes.

The cell divides again, this time one chromosome from each pair ends up in the new cell, making four cells each with two chromosomes.

Step 1

Step 2

How do you grow a seedless grape?

To understand how this is possible, we first need to understand what happens when plants produce seeds.

Flowers normally produce either male sex cells, **pollen**, or female sex cells, **ovules**. After pollination has taken place, the pollen that sticks to the stigma begins to grow in a **pollen tube**. This grows down the inside of the style, towards the ovules, which are found in the ovary of the plant. Once an ovule has been reached, the male nucleus travels down the pollen tube and fuses with it. Seeds develop from the fertilised ovule and can then germinate into new plants.

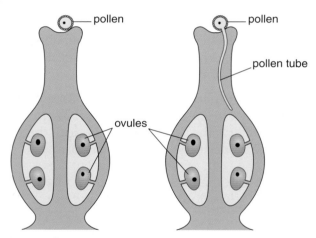

Figure 4   Pollen tube growing down the style towards the ovules.

Plants normally produce seeds once fertilisation of the ovule has taken place. The seed can be contained in fruits, such as grapes, oranges and lemons. The fruits are then eaten by animals and the seeds within the fruits are scattered in their droppings. Seeds are a nuisance to us as we normally have to spit them out.

Growing a seedless plant is simple. Plants have special chemicals called **hormones** that control how they grow as well as other things such as producing fruit, dropping leaves and fruit at the right time of year or simply growing roots. By spraying the grapevines with the hormone that controls fruiting, the plant can be forced to produce fruits, even though no fertilisation has taken place.

Not all plants produce fruits with seeds. Bananas, for example, are naturally seedless. The male flowers are sterile – which means that they cannot produce the male sex cell or pollen. It is the female flowers that produce the fruit. The plant grows from an underground stem called a **rhizome**. New shoots grow up and clumps of bananas called 'hands' grow where the female flowers were. Banana plants only live for one year and produce one crop of bananas then they die off. A new banana plant pops up from the underground shoot to make a new plant.

Figure 5   The banana plant might look like a tree but it is in fact a flowering plant.

What is a species?

Remember the work you did earlier on classification? I bet you can't remember what my real name is?

For two plants or animals to be the same species, they must be able to breed with each other to produce fertile young. For example, all domestic cats belong to the same genes and species (*Felis domesticus*). No matter what the variety of cat, Siamese, Persian, etc. they can all mate with one another and produce kittens that can also mate with other cats and have kittens.

The quagga (which became extinct in 1883) was originally thought to be different from the three other zebra species, but it was noticed that some plains zebra living today had incomplete striping and were coloured a similar brown colour to the quagga. When quagga DNA (from a stuffed foal in a museum) was tested in the early 1980s, it was found to be almost identical to that of the plains zebra. That meant that quagga genes were still around in the DNA of plains zebra.

By carefully selecting plains zebras with characteristics similar to quaggas, such as reduced striping or legs with no stripes scientists have managed to breed zebra that are beginning to look like quaggas.

Revision

Make a thinklinks map using the key words from this chapter. How many links can you make?

Questions

1 What are the two types of sex cells found in

  a) humans

  b) plants?

2 Where are the chromosomes found in the cells of plants and animals?

3 What is a gene?

4 Why are children similar, but not identical, to their natural parents?

5 Why are identical twins more similar than brothers and sisters?

6 Can identical twins be brother and sister? Explain your answer.

7 Border Collies, sometimes known as Welsh Sheep Dogs, were specially bred for herding farm animals. Is this an example of natural selection or artificial selection? Explain your choice.

8 What do the ovules normally develop into after they have fertilised?

9 What type of chemical do you think rooting powder contains to help cuttings from plants grow?

10 What do biologists mean when they call an animal a 'variety'?

11 What are the problems in trying to clone new animals from the old DNA of extinct animals?

The human body

2.1 Respiration

Key Words

aerobic	cellular
arteries	respiration
alveolus	energy
anaerobic	haemoglobin
blood	respiration
bronchus	trachea
capillaries	veins

Believe me, it takes a lot of energy to hop around all day, I spend a lot of time just eating.

How do cells use food?

We use sugar in the form of glucose as a fuel in our cells, where energy is released. This energy is used in different ways in the body. If there is a plentiful supply of oxygen, **energy** is released from glucose and carbon dioxide is produced. This reaction is called **respiration**. When it happens in our cells it is called **cellular** respiration.

> glucose + oxygen → carbon dioxide + water + ENERGY TRANSFER

The breakdown of glucose in cells really takes place in a series of small steps. Each step is made possible by the action of enzymes.

The blood system

Blood is the main transport system in our body. Oxygen and other substances, like glucose, are transported around our body by blood. Respiration takes place in every cell, so blood has to reach all of them to deliver glucose and oxygen.

The red blood cells transport oxygen. They contain a dark red substance called **haemoglobin**. As blood goes through the lungs, haemoglobin picks up oxygen from the air you breathe in. This oxygen is then released where it is needed as blood passes through tissues, close to cells.

Did you know that there are about 5000 million red blood cells in every 1 cm³ of blood?

Glucose is also transported to your cells and moves into them. As blood circulates, all the tissues will have access to a ready supply of oxygen and glucose.

Blood is mainly water and so it is very good at dissolving substances. Waste carbon dioxide is produced during respiration. This gas passes from the tissues into the blood where it dissolves in the plasma. The dissolved carbon dioxide is carried by blood to the lungs where it is released and breathed out.

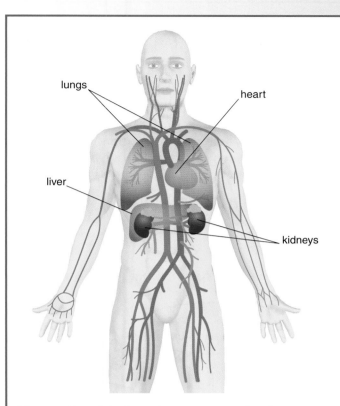

Figure 1 This shows how oxygen and carbon dioxide are transported around the body.

There are three main types of blood vessels: **arteries**, **veins** and **capillaries**.

Blood is pumped through arteries, away from the heart, to the tissues. In the tissues, the arteries get narrower and narrower until they form a network of capillaries. Capillaries have thin walls and pass very near cells. Because of the short distance between the capillaries and the cells, substances can move easily between the blood in the capillaries and cells in the tissues. After moving through tissues, blood is moved more slowly through veins back to the heart.

In the lungs there is a high concentration of oxygen from the air breathed in, so oxygen moves from the lungs into the blood where the concentration of oxygen is lower. Blood going to the lungs from the body tissues contains a higher concentration of waste carbon dioxide than the air breathed in, so carbon dioxide moves from the blood to the lungs to be breathed out. In muscles, the concentration effect makes these gases move the other way. Oxygen moves from the blood capillaries to muscle cells and carbon dioxide moves from muscle cells to the blood.

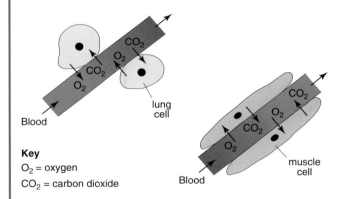

Key
O_2 = oxygen
CO_2 = carbon dioxide

Figure 2 As blood flows around tissues like the lungs and muscles, gases and other substances can move either from cells to the blood or from blood to the cells

Blood is pumped around the body by the **heart**. The heart walls are made from muscle that contracts, or beats, all the time. It pumps blood through tubes called **blood vessels** from the heart and back again. The heart has two pumps that work together. One side pumps blood to the lungs, the other side pumps blood to the other tissues.

Figure 3 *Arteries* have thick walls and take blood *away* from the heart. *Veins* have thinner walls and take blood *back to* the heart. *Capillaries* are tubes with very thin walls. They join arteries to veins

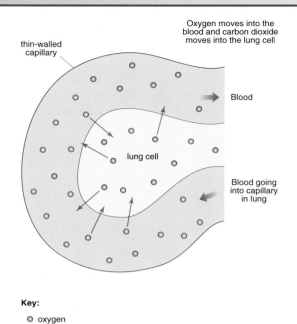

Figure 4 shows oxygen moving into the blood and carbon dioxide moving into the lung cell, with a thin-walled capillary, blood, lung cell, and blood going into capillary in lung labelled.

Key:
- ○ oxygen
- ○ carbon dioxide

Figure 4 With every breath you take, gases move across the capillary wall.

How do the lungs work?

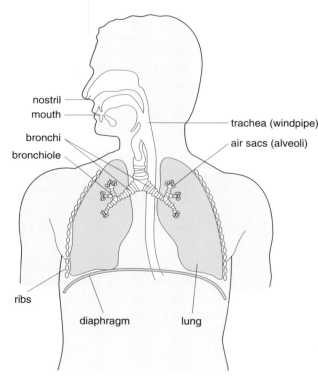

Labels: nostril, mouth, bronchi, bronchiole, trachea (windpipe), air sacs (alveoli), ribs, diaphragm, lung

Figure 5 This shows how air passes through your nose down into your lungs.

Air is drawn in through your nose and mouth, and then down air passages into two lungs, one on each side of your body. The trachea splits into two bronchi, one bronchus for each lung. The bronchi divide into many smaller tubes called bronchioles. The bronchioles end in millions of tiny air sacs called alveoli. The surface area of all the alveoli added together is very large. Plenty of gas can move between the capillaries and the alveoli because the alveoli:

- can hold large amounts of air
- have a large surface area
- have very thin walls
- have a good blood supply.

A single air sac is called an alveolus.

Aerobic and anaerobic respiration

There are two types of respiration: **aerobic** and **anaerobic**.

Aerobic literally means 'with oxygen' and anaerobic means 'without oxygen'.

Without oxygen, glucose is broken down in a different way, releasing energy and producing a substance called lactic acid. If lactic acid builds up, you get painful muscle pains called cramp and your muscles don't work properly.

Glucose → lactic acid + ENERGY TRANSFER

Respiration in plants and animals

Other living things respire in the same way as we do. When oxygen is available, they respire aerobically, producing carbon dioxide and water and releasing energy from their food.

Plants make their own glucose but respire in the same way as animals. The energy released from respiration in plants is used to draw substances in through the roots and move them around the plant. Energy is also used for growth and movement.

Revision

1 Enter each statement below under the correct heading, true or false.

a) In your lungs, carbon dioxide is taken into the blood.

b) In lungs, alveoli are surrounded closely by capillaries so that gases can easily pass between them.

c) Blood returns to the heart through veins.

d) Arteries have thicker walls than veins.

e) Blood being pumped to the tissues contains more oxygen than blood moving back to the heart.

f) Blocked arteries can cause a heart attack.

g) Aerobic respiration can only take place in the presence of oxygen.

h) Blood passes through the heart twice during a complete circuit of the body.

i) In anaerobic respiration, lactic acid and carbon dioxide are formed.

j) During exercise the volume of air you breathe in decreases.

k) Your pulse can be used to measure how fast you are exercising.

Questions

1 Name three things that our body does that require energy.

2 What do the following terms mean:

a) respiration

b) cellular respiration?

3 How is the fuel in a glucose tablet released as energy into your body?

4 Red blood cells and plasma are two of the parts of our blood. What other things do we find in our blood?

5 What would you expect a normal person's blood sugar level to do in the following situations:

a) after eating a light snack mid morning

b) after eating a normal school lunch of pizza, chips and a non-diet fizzy drink

c) after playing a school football/netball match

6 The heart muscle has its own blood supply through arteries called coronary arteries.

a) Why do you think the heart needs a plentiful supply of oxygen?

b) What do you think would happen if the coronary arteries were blocked?

c) Heart muscle is the same as any other muscle. What gas moves

i) from the blood capillaries to heart muscle

ii) from the heart muscle to the blood capillaries?

7 Write sentences to explain these scientific terms and ideas:

a) respiration in cells

b) blood plasma

c) red blood cells

d) white blood cells

e) gas transfer in the alveoli

f) the heart is two pumps

g) aerobic respiration

h) anaerobic respiration.

2.2 Food and digestion

Key Words

balanced diet
carbohydrate
colon
enzyme
fats
ileum

minerals
oesophagus
proteins
roughage
vitamins

You are what you eat!

In order to grow, remain healthy and have energy, we need food. The food that we eat is broken down in our digestive system and transported around the body by the bloodstream. The chemicals that make up our food can be grouped into seven types. Each of the seven types is needed to keep us healthy. A **balanced diet** contains the right amount of all seven types.

Food type	Common foods	Why we need them
Carbohydrates (chemicals made from carbon, hydrogen and oxygen) 	Bread, potatoes, rice, pasta, jam, sweets, fruit	These are energy-giving foods. Up to half of all the energy you need will come from carbohydrates.
Proteins 	Meat, fish, eggs, cheese, milk, bread	For growth and to repair damaged tissue. Muscles are mainly made up of protein. Some proteins can be used to give us energy.
Fats	Butter, cream, oils, meat, cheese, margarine	Up to 40% of the energy you need will come from fats. The body stores energy in the form of fat.
Minerals 	Cheese, milk (calcium)	Good for bones and teeth. A lack of calcium can lead to rickets.
	Liver, eggs, bread (iron)	Essential for making the chemical that transports oxygen around the body – haemoglobin (this also makes our blood red in colour).
	Salt (sodium)	Low sodium in our body can lead to cramp in the muscles.

Vitamins	A – liver, butter, green vegetables	Essential for good eyesight, especially in dim light.
	B_1 – bread, milk, potatoes, meat, yeast	
	B_2 – cheese, milk, liver, eggs	Mouth sores and dry skin are common if we lack vitamin B_2.
	B_{12} – meat, milk, yeast	A lack of vitamin B_{12} can lead to anaemia (a reduced number of red blood cells).
	C – oranges, lemons, fruits, green vegetables, tomatoes	A lack of vitamin C can cause scurvy (bleeding gums and internal bleeding).
	D – eggs, margarine, cod liver oil	Essential for healthy bones. A lack of vitamin D can lead to a disease called rickets (the bones are soft and can be bent out of shape as you grow).
Roughage (also known as fibre)	Vegetables, bread, cereals	Insoluble fibre increases the bulk of food and helps to keep the intestines working properly as the muscles in the intestines squeeze the fibre through.
Water	Many drinks, juices, milk and foods contain water	Two-thirds of your body mass is water. An adult needs to drink about 2.5 litres of water each day. Without any water, a human being will die very quickly.

Table 1   The seven food types

I eat flies and pondweed, what does that make me?

Digestion

It can take up to 24 hours for the food you eat to pass completely through your body. On its journey, the food is broken down and useful chemicals are absorbed into our blood and moved around the body. Anything that we eat that our body doesn't immediately need is either stored or, if that is not possible, excreted as waste. Figure 1 shows you what the human digestive system is like.

The first thing we do is break up food by chewing it. We use our teeth to cut, slice and grind the food, and saliva, containing an **enzyme**, begins to break down any starch and convert it to sugar.

Our tongues roll the food into a ball, or bolus, and it passes down the **oesophagus**.

In the stomach, the food and drink mixes with gastric juice. The juice contains hydrochloric acid to break down the food and an enzyme called pepsin that breaks down any protein into amino acids. The liquid in our stomachs is called chyme.

In your **small intestine**, the liver adds bile – this neutralises the acid and stops the fats clumping together. Enzymes break down what is left of the protein, carbohydrates and fats.

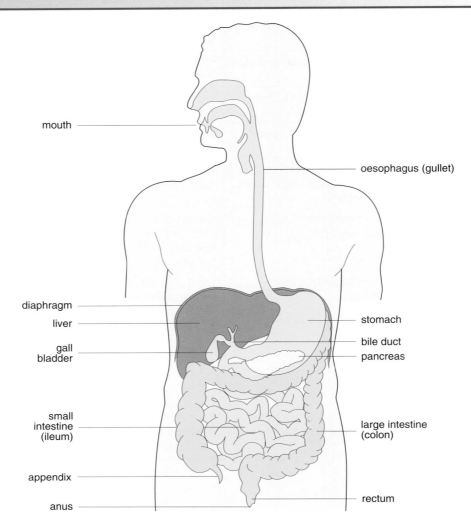

Figure 1 The human digestive system

As the liquid moves through the small intestine, the nutrients from the broken down food are absorbed into the bloodstream.

Bile also adds old, broken down red blood cells to the contents of our small intestine and this gives our waste an interesting brown colour . . . yuck!

By the time the liquid reaches the **colon** or large intestine (called 'large' because it is wider than the small intestine, not longer) all the useful parts of the food have been absorbed into the bloodstream and all that is left is waste, fibre and water. As water is very precious, the large intestine absorbs this back into the bloodstream so that all that is left is nearly solid waste. This we get rid of at regular intervals through the rectum and out through the anus.

Carbohydrates

Carbohydrates are chemicals made up of carbon, hydrogen and oxygen. They can be split into two groups, starches and sugars. Starch is a very large molecule, made up of lots of glucose molecules joined together in a long, mostly branching, chain.

There are lots of different types of sugars. They all end in the letters '**ose**'. One of the most useful to us is glucose. This is the sugar that gives us most of our energy. Sucrose is the sugar that we sprinkle into our tea or onto our food, glucose is used in some fizzy drinks, fructose is the sugar that makes fruits taste sweet and lactose is found in milk.

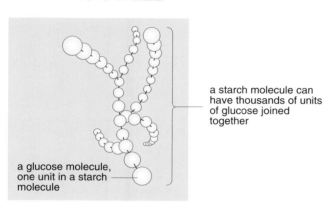

a starch molecule can have thousands of units of glucose joined together

a glucose molecule, one unit in a starch molecule

Figure 2   A long branching molecule of starch. Each unit in the chain is a molecule of glucose.

Proteins

Proteins are large molecules that can form chains. Protein chains are often folded. They are also made of units joined together. The units are called amino acids.

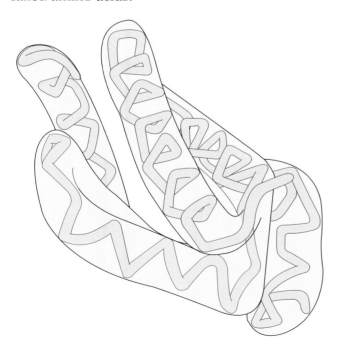

Figure 3   A protein molecule is a long chain that can be folded up.

Fats

Fats are also large molecules that are made up of two parts:

- fatty acids, which make up most of a fat molecule
- glycerol, which is similar to glucose.

We use fats to give us energy when we run out of glucose. When this happens, it is the glycerol that we use.

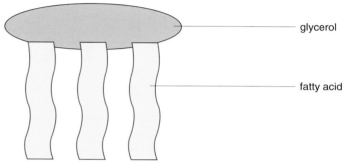

glycerol

fatty acid

Figure 4   A fat molecule, made up of a glycerol molecule with three fatty acid 'tails'.

Vitamins and minerals

Vitamins and minerals are very small molecules compared to the others we have talked about. They pass easily through the wall of the small intestine into our bloodstream without having to be digested first.

Enzymes

In order for all these molecules to be useful to us, we need to transport them around the body to places where we need them. For example, glucose needs to get into our muscle cells to give us energy. What our digestive system has to do is break down the large molecules to release those bits of the molecule that are useful to us so that they can pass through the cells in the wall of our small intestine. To do this we have special types of proteins called enzymes. Enzymes are mixed in with our food during digestion. Different types of enzymes act on different types of foods and they break them down into their units. The enzymes themselves are not changed or broken down, so can be used more than once to do the same job.

Hodder Science Summary Book

Revision

Using the key words from this section produce a thinklinks map linking them.

carbohydrate   colon   balanced diet   fats

enzyme   minerals   oesophagus   ileum   proteins

vitamins   roughage

Questions

1 Athletes eat very large amounts of food but rarely get fat. Why is this?

2 Good advice is to eat lots of fruit and fresh vegetables to keep healthy. Explain why people give this advice. Name two things that fruit and vegetables provide you with to help make up a balanced diet.

3 Which are the two food types that give us 90% of the energy we need? Where may we get the other 10% of our energy needs from?

4 Babies just need special milk to provide them with their balanced diet. Make a list of the things that milk contains.

5 Which mineral do babies store in their liver that is not provided in milk?

6 What does the term 'obese' mean?

7 Your body can store fat easily, but it cannot store vitamins. What happens if you take in more vitamins than your body can use?

8 It can take up to 24 hours to fully digest a meal. Why do you think it takes this long and what advantage is there in taking so long to digest food?

9 Saliva in the mouth and hydrochloric acid in the stomach can break up starch. Bread and pasta are rich in starch. Where are these types of foods mainly digested?

10 What is an enzyme?

2.3 Micro-organisms and disease

Coughs and sneezes spread diseases, so I catch them in my handkerchief.

AATISHOO!

Microbes

The word microbe is used to describe any microscopic organism whether it is useful or harmful to us. Germs are **microscopic** organisms called **viruses** and **bacteria**. There are millions of different types of bacteria and viruses.

There are more different types of bacteria on Earth than all the other living things put together!

If you compare a bacterium (plural bacteria) to a virus, there are a number of differences. A bacterium is much bigger than a virus. Bacteria have a similar structure to normal cells, but they do not have a nucleus. Bacteria contain strands of DNA instead. These control what happens in the bacterium and how it reproduces. Bacteria need a food supply to give them energy to enable them to grow and multiply. Many bacteria are involved in the decomposition (rotting) of dead plant and animal material.

Viruses do not have any of the structures found in normal cells. They do not need food to supply them with energy. They contain a strand of DNA and need to enter a cell of another organism to reproduce. Instead of a membrane surrounding the virus, they have a coat or shell made of protein. A virus can exist for thousands of years unchanged and inactive. Once it finds a new host cell it can become active again. The DNA strand then tells the host cell to make copies of the virus.

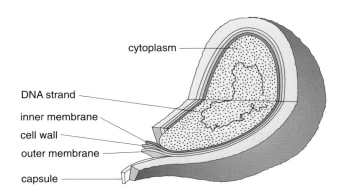

cytoplasm

DNA strand

inner membrane

cell wall

outer membrane

capsule

Figure 1   A simple bacterium

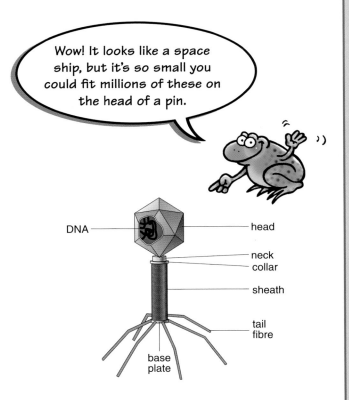

Wow! It looks like a space ship, but it's so small you could fit millions of these on the head of a pin.

DNA

head

neck
collar

sheath

tail
fibre

base
plate

Figure 2   A T2 phage virus which attacks bacteria

More micro-organisms

Yeast, penicillin and the cause of athlete's foot are also micro-organisms. They are all members of the fungus family. A **fungus** is a type of mould that lives in dark, warm, moist areas.

Yeast is a type of fungus. It is a very simple organism that can quickly reproduce by dividing in two. As it grows and respires it produces two waste products, the gas carbon dioxide and alcohol. The carbon dioxide causes the dough to rise in bread. In brewing beers, wines or spirits, yeast produces the alcohol.

Athlete's foot is another type of fungus. On the feet, the fungus can grow on and between toes, as well as on soles and toenails.

Spreading disease

There are a number of different ways in which **diseases** can be spread

1   Person-to-person: The spread of **infection** may involve the passing of bacteria and/or viruses by blood or saliva or, for very contagious (easily caught) diseases, through the air (see below).

2   Food-borne infection: Food poisoning caused by bacteria is an example of this. For example, bacteria can contaminate rice and survive boiling. If the rice is cooled and reheated, the bacteria may grow and produce a poison that makes you vomit.

3   Water-borne infection: Contaminated water can spread diseases such as typhoid, cholera, dysentery and polio.

4   Airborne infection: *Legionella pneumophila* is the bacteria that causes Legionnaire's disease. It can be found in many natural water sources but is normally found in poorly-maintained air-conditioning systems or rarely-cleaned shower heads. Airborne droplets of water can be breathed in causing an infection.

5   Insect-borne infection: Many diseases are spread by insects. The plague, for example, was carried by rat fleas.

Internal army

AATISHOO!

> Your body can fight off a lot of the micro-organisms that cause infection.

Your body's defences

Almost half of your blood is made up of cells – **red blood cells, white blood cells** and fragments of cells called **platelets**.

White blood cells are made in your bone marrow. Some of them are then changed by the thymus gland into different types of white blood cell to help fight off different types of infection. White cells can gather together in your spleen, tonsils, adenoids, appendix and small intestine. They can also gather in the lymph nodes. The **lymph** system contains a colourless fluid which transports white blood cells to the site of infection and micro-organisms and dead cells back to the lymph nodes where they can be broken down and removed from the body.

Your **immune** system has developed a number of ways of defending against invading micro-organisms. One of the first barriers is your skin. In case you breathe in any micro-organisms, hairs in your nose and tiny hair-like projections on the surface of cells lining the entrance to your lungs are coated in a sticky mucus. This traps the invaders and passes them upward and out of the body when you cough, sneeze and blow your nose

If you breathe in small amounts of micro-organisms or get any blown into your eyes, enzymes in your saliva and tears will destroy them. If you eat or drink something that contains small amounts of bacteria, the acid in your stomach will kill them. If you cut yourself and bacteria get into the cut, they will quickly divide and multiply. To try and stop them getting into your bloodstream, your body increases the supply of blood to the injured area, making it appear red and warm, bringing white blood cells to destroy the invaders. Fluid leaks into the surrounding tissue which is why you get a swelling. To stop the blood from continuously leaking, platelets gather around the wound and begin to form a small clot. This plugs the hole in the blood vessel and forms a scab on the surface of the skin. The scab also helps to stop micro-organisms from entering the body.

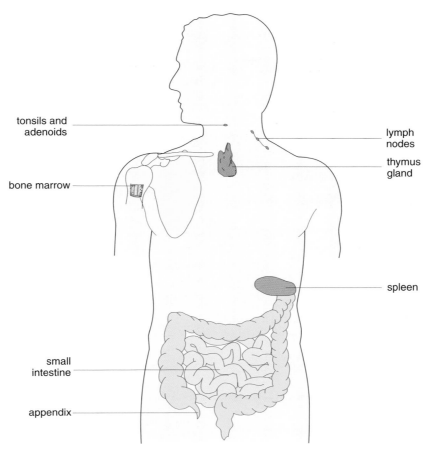

Figure 3   Disease-fighting organs

Revision

1   Try making a thinklinks map using the key words listed at the start of this section. Make as many links as you can and explain what the links are.

Questions

1   When you put your finger on your wrist, you can feel your pulse. What is your pulse and where does it come from?

2   Gardeners often get cuts on their hands. Explain why it is important to cover a cut with sticking plaster, no matter how small the cut.

3   What can micro-organisms do if they get into our bodies?

4   What foods/drinks are made with the direct help of micro-organisms?

5   Which parts of normal cells are not present in viruses?

6   Water-borne diseases are much more common in less economically developed countries. Why might this be the case?

7   If you accidentally cut yourself, describe what would happen and explain the following:

   a) why you stop bleeding after a while

   b) why the area around the cut goes red

   c) why the area around the cut feels warm.

8   List the organs and glands in the body that are there to try and protect you from disease.

9   Apart from special organs, in what other ways does our body protect us from getting infected with micro-organisms?

2.4 Fit and healthy

Key Words

alveoli (alveolus)	ileum
bronchi (bronchus)	intercostal
	oesophagus
bronchioles	organ system
cirulatory	rectum
colon	respiratory
diaphragm	trachea
digestive	

Healthy systems

Three **organ systems** have to work together to keep us fit and healthy; the **respiratory**, **digestive** and **circulatory** systems. Another two, the skeletal and muscle systems, are essential for support and movement.

The respiratory system includes the air passages, such as the **trachea** and **bronchi**, the lungs, including the **bronchioles** and **alveoli**, and the muscles that control breathing, such as the **intercostal** muscles (the muscles between the ribs) and the **diaphragm**.

The digestive system breaks down food into its basic chemical parts, so that the body can absorb them and use them to release energy and for growth. This system includes the mouth, the **oesophagus**, the stomach, the small and large intestine (ileum and colon), the gall bladder, the pancreas, the liver and the **rectum**.

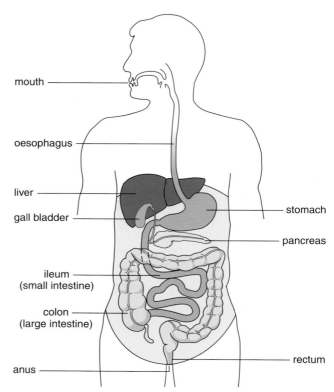

Figure 2   The digestive system

The circulatory system is made up of the **heart** and **blood vessels**. These provide a continuous flow of blood around the body, providing all our tissues with oxygen and nutrients and taking away any waste products.

The **skeletal system** gives us a body shape and works with our muscles to allow us to move or lift things. Our arms and legs act like levers. The skeletal system is made up of the bones of the skeleton and the different types of joints between the bones.

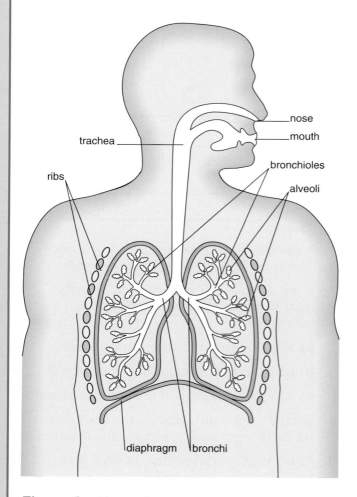

Figure 1   The respiratory system

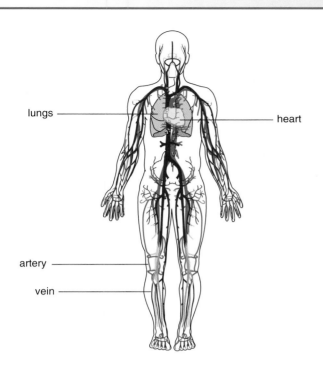

Figure 3 The circulatory system

The **muscle system** is made up of all of the muscles of the body and the tendons that attach the muscles to the bones, or to each other. Ligaments are made of tough elastic tissue. They bind together the ends of bones and help prevent excessive movements of the joints during exercise.

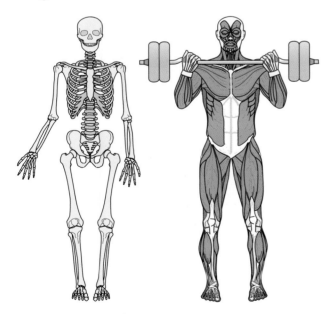

Figure 4 The skeletal and muscle systems

Diet, exercise and fitness

Fitness is about how we eat, look after ourselves and keep the organs and organ systems in tip-top condition. To be fit and healthy, you must:

- eat a balanced diet

- do a reasonable amount of exercise

- not take drugs other than those prescribed for us.

And as an adult you should not:

- smoke or drink excess alcohol.

Very active people, such as athletes and those with physical jobs, need lots of energy from food. People who are less active or who have sedentary jobs (jobs that don't require them to move around a lot, like office work) need less energy. Men usually need more energy than women and adolescents can need more than adults as they are still growing. Exercise is also important for fitness.

Smoking and health

There are three chemicals in tobacco smoke that can be harmful. They are nicotine, carbon monoxide and tar.

Nicotine is a powerful chemical that is addictive. Nicotine acts like a tranquilliser, but it is actually a stimulant.

Carbon monoxide is a gas. It is similar to carbon dioxide, but is very dangerous. The gas is colourless, odourless and poisonous, and in large amounts can kill. Smokers only take in small amounts of carbon monoxide, but over a long period of time it decreases the amount of oxygen that reaches the tissues in the body and can lead to a build up of fatty deposits in the arteries. This means the heart has to work harder and can lead to heart attacks.

Tar in cigarettes deposits a layer of chemicals on the respiratory tract (the trachea, bronchi, bronchioles and alveoli). This can lead to difficulty in breathing. The tar also contains chemicals that can cause cancer.

Smoking and cancer

Smokers suffer from higher rates of mouth cancer, cheek cell cancer and lung cancer than non-smokers. 90% of lung cancer deaths are linked with smoking, and 30% of all cancer-related deaths are caused by tobacco. Lung cancer is not the only type of cancer associated with smoking. There are also links with lip cancer, bladder cancer and in women, cervical cancer (the cervix is the entrance to the womb).

Smoking and other diseases

Emphysema

This is a disease that stops people from breathing properly.

Tobacco smoke causes the tiny air sacs in the lungs – the alveoli – to become less elastic and to fuse together. This makes them less efficient and reduces the surface area of the lungs available to let oxygen into the bloodstream and carbon dioxide out.

Strokes

This is where part of the brain is damaged by a lack of blood supply.

Heart attacks

This happens when the heart muscle is deprived of blood.

Women who smoke while they are pregnant risk harming their unborn baby. The chemicals in the tobacco smoke pass into the mother's bloodstream and are transferred across the placenta into the unborn baby's bloodstream. Because the baby is so much smaller, the effects of small amounts of chemicals are greater than on the adult mother.

Figure 5 Cigarette companies have to put health warnings on all packets of cigarettes.

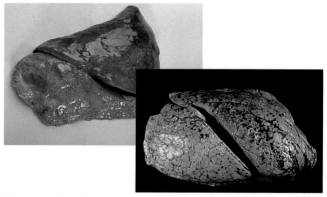

Figure 6 The smoker's lung on the right is less efficient and the tissue has become hardened and blackened by the effects of tobacco smoke.

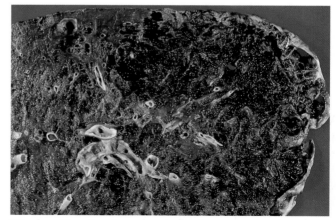

Figure 7 Emphysema means that not enough oxygen is reaching the tissues. This photo shows a lung from a smoker with emphysema.

Alcohol

Alcohol units

One unit of alcohol is equal to ½ pint of ordinary beer or lager, one glass of wine or one pub measure of a spirit, such as whisky or vodka.

Figure 8

Some drinks may have a different level of alcohol from this so many manufacturers now label their bottled drinks with the number of units they contain to help people measure how much they are drinking.

Alcohol and health

Alcohol can affect many different cells, tissues and organs in your body. The organ most at risk is the liver. Heavy drinking destroys liver cells and eventually the liver can stop working.

Heavy drinking can also lead to:

- stomach problems including stomach cancer and ulcers (where the lining of the stomach is being eaten away by the stomach acid)
- cancers of the mouth, tongue, throat and oesophagus
- brain tissue damage.

Women who drink while they are pregnant are risking their unborn baby's health. The alcohol enters the bloodstream and is passed along the umbilical cord into the baby's bloodstream. Because the baby is so much smaller and its cells, tissues and organs are still developing the effects of alcohol are greater than on the adult mother.

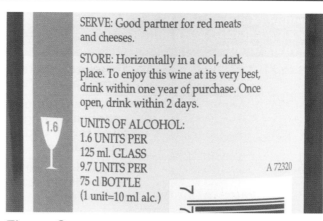

SERVE: Good partner for red meats and cheeses.

STORE: Horizontally in a cool, dark place. To enjoy this wine at its very best, drink within one year of purchase. Once open, drink within 2 days.

1.6

UNITS OF ALCOHOL:
1.6 UNITS PER
125 ml. GLASS
9.7 UNITS PER
75 cl BOTTLE
(1 unit=10 ml alc.)

A 72320

Figure 9

Drugs and health

Drugs can be divided into three groups: recreational, medicinal and illegal. All drugs can be dangerous if they are used in the wrong way.

Recreational drugs

Caffeine is an example. This is found naturally in coffee beans, tea leaves and cocoa beans. It is also put into some soft drinks, such as cola, artificially. Caffeine increases the nerve activity in the brain. Large amounts of caffeine can cause your hands to tremble and it feels like your heart is racing.

Other recreational drugs are not as harmless, but they are still legal for adults to buy. These include nicotine and alcohol.

Medicinal drugs

All medicines should only be taken according to the instructions and only when you really need them. Paracetamol, a common painkiller, could kill you if you take too many at once or don't follow the instructions carefully. The problem is that the drug can damage your liver, and once this happens it cannot be reversed.

Some prescribed drugs are just as addictive and dangerous as illegal drugs, but doctors know how much to give to make sure that the drug is not causing any problems.

Illegal drugs

There are many different types of illegal drugs. They all change the way a person feels or think they feel. There are many different types of illegal drugs, including cocaine, heroin, cannabis, acid and ecstacy.

Number of units a week for an adult male over 18 years of age	Too much or not?	Number of units a week for an adult female over 18 years of age
Up to 21	These are generally safe limits for healthy normal adults if spread over the week.	Up to 14
22–25	This level of drinking may not damage your health long-term, but if you drink all of this in two or three sessions it will cause damage.	15–21
36–49	Regularly drinking this much in a week will cause long-term damage to your health.	22–35
50 or more	Drinking this much regularly will definitely cause serious damage to your health and you may even become dependent on alcohol – this means it will be difficult for you to cut down or give up.	36 or more

Table 2   Guidelines for safe drinking

Revision

1   Make some revision cards that contain key points or information for you to learn about the following things. Your cards may also contain diagrams to help you.

muscle system   **health**   **skeletal system**   **recreational drugs**

diet   **medicinal drugs**   **illegal drugs**   **tobacco**

fitness   **smoking**   **digestive system**

Questions

1 What are the six different food groups needed to maintain a balanced diet?

2 Which two food groups give us nearly all of our energy and, of these, which one gives us most energy?

3 What is the name of the addictive chemical found in tobacco smoke?

4 If there were 36 276 deaths from lung cancer in a year, using information in this section calculate how many of these could be linked to tobacco?

5 If there were 118 000 deaths from all types of cancer in a year, how many would be linked to tobacco?

6 What is the effect of nicotine on the arteries?

a) Would they get narrower or wider?

b) What happens to the blood supply?

c) What effect does this have on the heart?

7 When someone is thought to be alcohol dependent, what does this mean?

8 Why is drinking alcohol and driving or operating machines dangerous?

9 Many illegal drugs are known as 'mind-altering'. What do you think this means?

10 What is the difference between the following groups of drugs:

a) recreational

b) medicinal or prescription

c) illegal?

CHAPTER 3

Living things and the environment

3.1 Habitats, adaptation and chains

Key Words

carnivore
decomposer
ecologist
food chain
food web
habitat
herbivore
life cycle
omnivore
producer
primary
  consumer
secondary
  consumer
temperate

Of course all I need is a nice 'pad' of my own.

a) moors

b) rocky coast

A place to live

We live in what is called a **temperate** region. This means that the weather is neither tropical (hot and humid) nor polar (cold and icy). Living organisms can adapt successfully to different habitats.

Jungles, deserts and ice palaces

Living things have been found in all types of places around the world, from deep in the ice of Antarctica to the murky depths of the oceans. Living things adapt to the conditions they find themselves in. Where a plant or animal lives naturally is called its **habitat**.

Even in the UK we have different habitats that contain different types of plants and animals

c) woodland

Figure 1   Some different habitats in the UK

35

which have adapted to where they live. Figure 1 shows some of these habitats.

Scientists called **ecologists** conduct surveys of habitats and list the different types of plants and animals they find there. They also study what happens to habitats when they are damaged by human activity or pollution.

The urban fox

Foxes usually live in the countryside. They eat a wide variety of things including rabbits and other small mammals. Many foxes now live in the cities. They are called urban foxes (Figure 2). They live off the rubbish that humans put out and on any small mammals they can catch. The urban fox has learned to survive in the cities. People driving home late at night often see urban foxes on the roads.

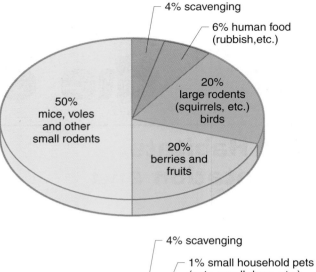

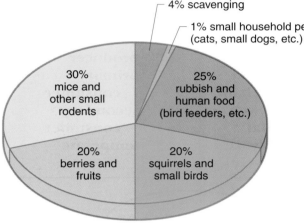

Figure 3   Comparing the diets of a country fox (top) and an urban fox (bottom)

Look at the two pie charts showing what foxes eat. Think about how the urban foxes have adapted their diet to living in the city.

A year in the life of a fox

As a red fox grows up, it goes through a number of different stages as part of its **life cycle**.

The red fox, *Vulpes vulpes*, is found in many countries, from North and South America to Africa, Asia and all through Europe. It is a common sight in the countryside and is becoming more and more common in our towns and cities.

Foxes have adapted very well to the growth of towns and cities. As more farm and meadow land has been built on, foxes have learned to live among people. They no longer eat meadow creatures, such as rabbits, or steal chickens from

Figure 2   An urban fox raiding a bin for food

If you dig a pond, it won't be long before us frogs find it. Actually we often get carried to ponds as frog spawn on the feet of birds.

Figure 4   A vixen with her cubs

farms. Now they get a lot of their food by scavenging in people's dustbins and around houses in towns.

How an animal or plant lives, grows, develops and eventually dies can be summed up in what we call a **life cycle**.

Figure 6   A simple food chain

Figure 5   The life cycle of a frog (a) Eggs or spawn are laid in the water and then fertilised by the male frog. (b) A tadpole, that lives and swims in water appears after about a week. (c) Five weeks later, it starts growing legs and lungs. (d) The frog is ready to grow up and lay eggs or fertilise eggs. This takes about two years.

Step number	Name	Plant/animal type
1	**Producer** Something that makes or produces its own food.	green plants
2	**Primary consumer** Primary means first and consumer means to eat, so this level contains animals that eat plants.	insects and herbivores (animals that only eat plants)
3	**Secondary consumer** At this level the animals are usually (but not always) larger and they will hunt other animals.	usually carnivores (animals that eat other animals) and omnivores (animals that eat both plants and animals)
4	**Decomposer** When plants and animals die, their bodies are broken down and nutrients are put back into the soil. (We don't normally include decomposers in food chains.)	fungi and bacteria

Table 1 The components of food chains and webs

Food chains and webs

Food chains and webs show us how energy is transferred from one living organism to another.

Very few animals eat only one type of food. Most animals, including humans, eat lots of different foods. Many **food chains** can be linked together forming **food webs**.

Food webs give scientists a better idea of who eats what or whom in real life. Food webs can be very complicated, but like food chains they always start with plants that make their own food.

Figure 8 The creatures in the food chain on Bear Island in the Arctic. Plants → insects → sandpipers → Arctic fox

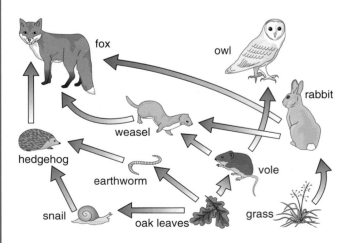

Figure 7 A woodland food web

Survival!

> You know some of my distant cousins have a coating of slimy poisonous chemicals that could kill a predator if they tried to eat them.

Some animals and plants have adapted ways of helping them survive predators.

Being part of a food chain or web is dangerous unless you happen to be at the top. Many plants and animals have had to develop ways of protecting themselves from being eaten by others.

Plants have a number of ways of protecting themselves against being eaten. Some plants are poisonous, others have a bad taste or burn the mouth, like chillies and peppers. Yet more have developed to look like poisonous plants although they are not.

Animals have developed many ways of protecting themselves, from armour plating to sharp teeth and claws or camouflage or the ability to out-run other animals.

Figure 8   Plant and animal adaptations

An eagle has excellent eyesight and a sharp beak and talons (claws).

Meerkats. They stand on their back legs, looking out for predators.

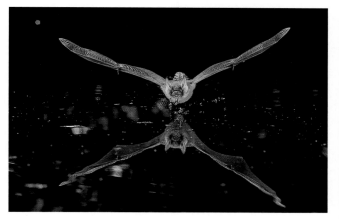

A bat uses high pitched sounds to locate its prey.

A spider spins a sticky web to catch flies and other insects.

Chillies have a 'hot' chemical to warn animals off that try to eat the plant.

A stick insect looks like a stick and is almost invisible to predators.

Cacti have sharp spines that stop animals eating them.

A dover sole uses camouflage to hide on the sea floor.

A snowshoe hare in summer (left) and winter (right) changes the colour of its fur to try and camouflage itself.

Revision

Complete the following passage using the words supplied.

**predators   habitats cacti   primary carnivores   photosynthesis animals
urban fox   camouflage   spines   food web   producers**

Different ____**1**____ support different plants and ____**2**____. In a jungle habitat, animals often have colourful markings that they use for ____**3**____. In the desert, plants such as ____**4**____ will have thick fleshy stems that hold a lot of water. The cactus has small, modified leaves that look like ____**5**____. These stop water evaporating and protect the plant from ____**6**____. Some animals such as the ____**7**____, can adapt to different environments. It has learned to live in the city instead of its native countryside.

Plants are called ____**8**____ because they make their own food. They make sugar by a process called ____**9**____. Animals that eat plants only are called herbivores. They are ____**10**____ consumers. Animals that eat other animals are called secondary consumers or ____**11**____. Plants and animals are found in food chains. A food chain shows how the energy from the Sun is transferred from plants to animals and on to other animals. Lots of food chains are present in any habitat and these form a ____**12**____.

Questions

1 The panda only eats bamboo and the koala will only eat eucalyptus leaves.

   a) Why do nearly all other animals eat more than one type of food?

   b) What problems could there be in only eating one food type?

2 Explain how the following plants and animals are adapted to their habitat?

   a) polar bear

   b) camel

   c) zebra

   d) cactus

   e) thorn bush

3 Explain what 'adapted' means.

4 Write one food chain for each habitat on page 35. Remember to include a plant at the start, an animal that eats plants and an animal that eats other animals.

5 Every food chain has a big animal at its end. What do these animals have in common?

6 Plants and animals adapt to the changing seasons in different ways. How do the following adapt to the changing seasons

   a) an oak tree

   b) a brown bear?

7 Humans adapt to different habitats using technology. We inhabit a large number of places on Earth, but there are still places where we cannot survive. List some places on Earth where humans cannot survive without special clothes and equipment to help us.

8 Explain how we are able to visit:

   a) the Antarctic and what special clothing you may need

   b) the Great Barrier Reef in Australia and what special equipment/clothing you may need.

9 Plants produce or make their own food. Where do plants get the energy from to do this?

10 What do the following terms mean:

   a) primary producer

   b) secondary producer

   c) herbivore

   d) carnivore

   e) omnivore?

3.2 Ecological relationships

Key Words

food chain
food web
population
predator
prey

pyramid of numbers
pyramid of biomass

Populations

Human beings make up what we call a **population**. There are lots of other types of plants and animals on Earth. These also make up populations.

Populations of plants and animals try to reach a state of balance between those starting life and those dying. External factors will often change the balance. Seasons will change, and with them the food supply. As the population of one plant or animal increases, so will the population of those that feed on it. The populations will then find a balance at a new, higher level.

Sometimes the environment changes so much that an entire population dies out. This is called **extinction**. Extinction can occur naturally or be caused by human activity such as deforestation or destroying a natural habitat for farming or building.

How many people are there in the world today?

The world's population is growing rapidly.

The United Nations say that the six billionth baby was a baby boy born in the Bosnian capital, Sarajevo, at 2 minutes past midnight local time on Tuesday 12 October 1999. The UN chose this as 'D6B', the Day of the six Billionth person.

Predator vs prey

A **predator** is an animal that hunts, catches and eats other animals for food. The animals being hunted are called **prey**. Predators help to keep the numbers of prey down in an area and, in turn, the number of prey in an area will limit the numbers of predators that can live there.

If the two species have lived in the same area for a long time, the prey learn to deal with the predator, and try not to be caught and eaten. Therefore, the predator kills mainly the weakest prey. Animals are not necessarily always predators or always prey. For example, a stickleback fish may hunt and eat tadpoles, but it may also be hunted and eaten itself by a roach. Any animal that is prey must somehow try to survive. In other words it must try to adapt. Some adaptations give the prey an advantage over the predator, like speed or flight, some are designed to fool the predator and others hide the prey.

False features that appear to be enormous eyes or appendages can fool potential predators, as can making yourself look bigger than you are.

Pretending to be an animal that is dangerous to a predator is also a means of avoiding being eaten. Some animals' physical features make them a very undesirable meal. Hedgehogs, for example, are very difficult for predators to eat because of their extremely sharp spines.

Figure 1 The puffer fish inflates its body to make it difficult to eat and to make it appear larger than it really is.

Figure 2 The colour of the frog and its markings warn any predators that it should not be eaten.

Chemical features can be just as effective. The poison arrow frog (see Figure 2) also uses chemicals (poisons secreted from its skin) to deter attackers. Any animals that eat these small frogs are likely to get very sick or die.

Figure 3 The hedgehog's spines make it a difficult meal to eat.

Some animals blend into the background as their colour and the patterns on their skin or coats hide them from potential danger.

Predators, on the other hand, also adapt. They develop ways of searching out their prey. Those with the best eyesight, keenest hearing and/or greatest sense of smell will have more success in finding food than predators with poor senses.

Looking at pyramids

When we look at **food chains** and **food webs** we can see how energy is being transferred from plants to animals and on to other animals in the chain or web. We can also look at numbers of organisms and how energy is transferred by looking at **pyramids of numbers** and **pyramids of biomass.**

Pyramids of numbers

If you look at a simple food chain in a pond, you will see that one piece of pondweed can feed a lot of tadpoles. Also, one minnow might eat a lot of tadpoles, one perch might eat a lot of minnows, and one heron might eat a lot of perch. Trying to make a pyramid of numbers is not easy! It might look something like Figure 4. A pyramid of numbers is not always very helpful. It doesn't tell us, for example, how the energy is transferred and wasted as we move up the pyramid or chain. Instead ecologists use a pyramid of biomass. This tells us much more about the transfer of energy.

Pyramids of biomass

If we took a complete pond and removed all of the pondweed and weighed it, we could find out its biomass. (Biomass is simply a fancy way of saying how much of a living thing there is – its mass. Remember in science we measure mass in kilograms.) If we do the same for the tadpoles, the minnows, the perch and the herons we would get a pyramid that looks like the one in Figure 4. There is less mass and therefore less energy as we move up the pyramid, so at each step we are wasting some of the energy. (Remember also that we cannot create or destroy energy, we can only transfer it.)

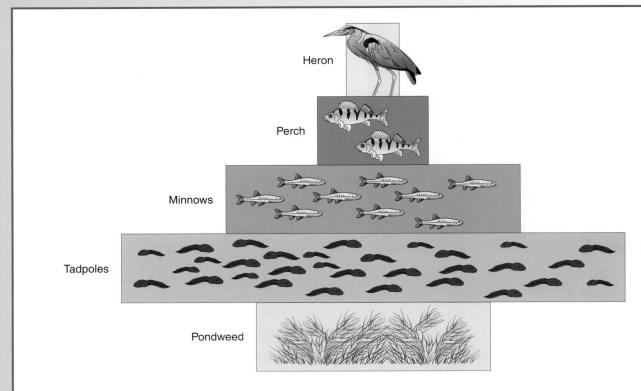

Figure 4 A pyramid of numbers

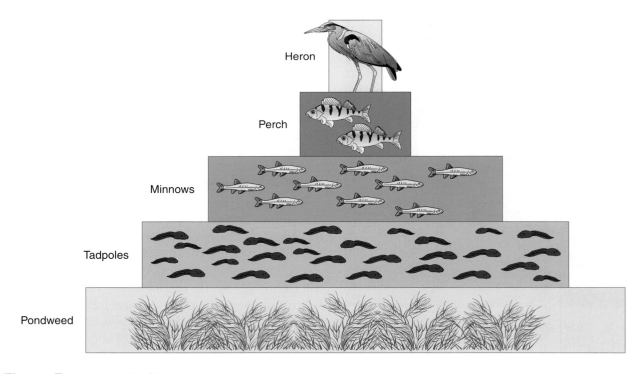

Figure 5 A pyramid of biomass

The killing chain

Food chains show us how energy is transferred from plants to animals and on to other animals. It isn't just energy that can be transferred – pesticides sprayed on plants or put into streams and rivers to control insects and other pests can also be transferred. In the 1960s and 1970s one particular pesticide, **DDT**, caused a lot of damage as it was transferred through the food chain.

The proper chemical name for DDT is DichloroDiphenylTrichloroethane, not an easy name to remember, which is why scientists prefer to call it DDT.

DDT was widely used to kill off harmful insects which were destroying crops. It was later found that DDT could be harmful to more than just the insects. A lot of DDT was found in many animal species including fish, birds and mammals, as well as some plant species.

Figure 6 shows how DDT travelled along a food chain. DDT entered the rivers after being sprayed on crops. It then entered zooplankton – microscopic one-celled animals – that were eaten by small fish. The small fish were eaten by larger fish which were, in turn, eaten by fish-eating birds such as herons.

Revision

1 Match the following terms with their definition.

Term	Definition
Pyramid of numbers	shows how energy is transferred from one living thing to another.
Food chain	shows us how many individuals there are in a food chain or a food web.
Food web	shows us how much the individuals in a food chain or web would weigh.
Pyramid of biomass	is made up of many food chains and shows who eats what or whom.

2 Now create some definitions for the words below.

- food chains
- habitat
- photosynthesis
- adaptation
- producer
- primary consumer
- secondary consumer
- decomposer

zooplankton → small fish → large fish → heron.

Figure 6   DDT builds up in the food chain.

Questions

1 Here is a very simple food web.

What would happen to the different populations of animals if:

a) all the aphids died?

b) the sparrowhawks all died of DDT poisoning?

c) the great tit population was greatly reduced?

d) the oak tree lost its leaves for the winter?

2 What particular features do these animals have to help them catch prey?

a) scorpion

b) wild cat in the UK

c) cheetah

d) shark

3 What features do these animals have that often allow them to escape being another animal's meal?

a) snail

b) porcupine

c) turtle

d) gazelle

e) zebra

4 How would a pyramid of numbers look for the following food chain?

Rosebush (1) → Aphids (200) → Ladybirds (5) → Blackbird (2) → Cat (1)

5 Pesticides kill off the pests that can ruin crops. Less economically developed countries are still using DDT. Now that we know how harmful it can be, why are they still using DDT on their crops?

a) 10 000 joules of energy are transferred to a patch of grass by the Sun.

b) 9000 joules of this are reflected back. 1000 joules are stored by the grass as carbohydrate.

c) 100 joules are stored as food by rabbits that eat the grass. 900 joules are transferred to the environment by the rabbits as waste and heat.

d) 10 joules are stored as food by the fox that eats the rabbit. 90 joules are transferred to the environment as waste and heat by the fox.

6 As well as using pesticides, we also have insecticides and herbicides to kill off pests. What do these chemicals kill off?

7 The DDT didn't actually kill the large fish-eating birds directly. Why did the numbers of these birds reduce in a country that used DDT?

8 If the DDT was sprayed onto the crops in the fields, how did the chemical end up in the rivers?

9 Draw a food chain and energy transfer diagram using the information below. Put the energy values above the arrow in the food chain.

3.3 Plants, photosynthesis and food

Key Words	
photosynthesis	transpiration
carbon dioxide	herbicide
cholorophyll	pesticide
stomata (stoma)	insecticide

$$\text{carbon dioxide} + \text{water} \xrightarrow[\text{chlorophyll}]{\text{sunlight}} \text{glucose} + \text{oxygen}$$

Living on fresh air

Plants make their own food by a process called **photosynthesis**. Four things are needed for photosynthesis to occur: **sunlight**, **carbon dioxide**, **chlorophyll** and **water**. The speed of photosynthesis also depends on the temperature.

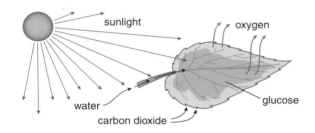

Figure 1   Photosynthesis in a leaf

Plants make their own food using energy from sunlight to join together water and the gas carbon dioxide from the air. The plant makes a type of sugar called glucose and produces the gas oxygen as a waste product. This process is known as photosynthesis. The word photosynthesis describes what the plant does – *photo* means light and *synthesis* means making, so plants *make* food *using* light. We can use a word formula to show this chemical process.

The carbon dioxide enters the leaf through tiny holes called **stomata**. (Stomata is the term used for lots of holes. One hole is called a **stoma**.) The oxygen that is made or produced goes back into the air through the same holes. Any part of a plant that is green can photosynthesise, but it mainly happens in the leaves. Most of the stomata are on the underside of the leaf, but there are some on the top of the leaf and on the stem. Plants cannot use all of the sugar that they make straight away and so they have to store some of it. To do this, they have to join units of sugar together to make starch (see page 25 for the structure of starch). They store the starch in their leaves for use when they cannot make food, for example in the dark.

When plants photosynthesise, they get bigger and heavier. This means the plant's biomass increases. The wood that makes up a tree, for example, has come mainly from the gases in the air and the water from the soil.

If a plant is going to photosynthesise, it must have four things:

- sunlight
- water
- carbon dioxide
- chlorophyll.

Three of these things – sunlight, water and carbon dioxide – will affect how much food a plant can make and how quickly it can make it. There is another factor that will affect how quickly and how much a plant will photosynthesise and that is the surrounding temperature. Just like animals, plants work best when the surrounding temperature is not too hot and not too cold.

Look at the three graphs below in Figure 2. They show what happens when the factors that affect photosynthesis in plants are changed.

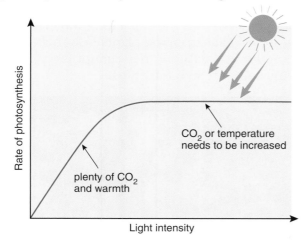

plenty of CO_2 and warmth

CO_2 or temperature needs to be increased

Light intensity

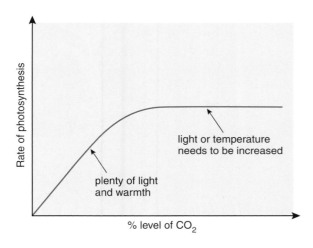

plenty of light and warmth

light or temperature needs to be increased

% level of CO_2

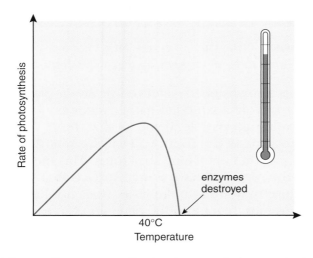

enzymes destroyed

40°C
Temperature

Figure 2 Factors affecting the rate of photosynthesis

Discovering photosynthesis

It's good this soil!

350 years ago, many people thought the soil gave the plant everything it needed to live and grow.

J.B. van Helmont did an experiment to see if soil provided food for plants. He took 90 kg of soil and a small willow tree. He weighed the tree and planted it into the soil. He only watered the tree and let it grow for five years.

After five years he weighed the tree, dried the soil and weighed that as well. The soil had only lost 0.5 kg but the tree had gained 77 kg. He thought that all of this must have come from the water. He wasn't quite right, but it was a good idea.

Figure 3

Roots

Roots are as important to a plant as its leaves. They have a number of roles, including taking water and minerals from the soil into the plant, and helping to anchor the plant in the ground.

Roots are very simple structures, but they are vital to plants. A root doesn't just help the plant, it also helps to maintain the soil and can break up rocks. The root's main job is to absorb water from the soil for the plant to use in photosynthesis. In Figure 4 you can see how the structure of the root helps the plant to take up water.

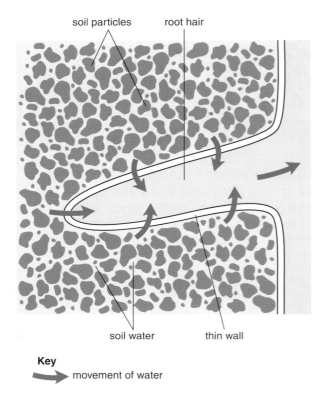

soil particles   root hair

soil water   thin wall

Key

movement of water

Figure 4   The thin wall of root hair lets water in easily.

The job of the root doesn't end there though. Roots have other jobs or functions. The root will anchor the plant in the soil and stop it from being blown over in the wind or easily uprooted when animals walk through it.

Roots come in two main types – **tap roots** and **fibrous roots**.

A tap root is a thick root that is long and extends down into the soil. This sort of root is useful if the soil dries out and the plant has to

go deeper to find water. Trees have tap roots and these sorts of roots stop them from being blown down easily, but they can be uprooted more easily than plants that have fibrous roots.

Fibrous roots are the ones that you see on many garden plants. They are thin and there are lots of them that spread out from the plant, but they do not go down into the soil a long way. These roots are good at stopping plants from being uprooted by animals but they cannot grow deep into the soil to search for water.

Figure 5   The tap root on the left is thick and long. The fibrous roots on the right are thin and widespread.

Just as humans need water to live, so do plants. The roots are adapted to gather water as efficiently as possible. If you look at the photograph of the roots, you will see that they are long, thin branching structures. This means that the roots will have a large surface area. Because they are thin the water does not have to travel far to get into the plant and can easily be moved from the roots up to the stem and leaves. Plants lose water from their leaves and this process is known as **transpiration**.

For plants to grow, they also need minerals. It is a bit like us having a balanced diet. The minerals are dissolved in the water in the soil and taken in through the roots. Plants need a balanced diet of minerals and other chemical salts for healthy growth. For example, magnesium is needed for the plant to make the chemical chlorophyll. To make plant proteins the plant needs nitrates and potassium from fertilisers added to the soil.

Plants for food and plant nutrients

We eat different parts of the plants we eat – leaves, shoots, roots, fruits and seeds. Plants need three main minerals to stay healthy – nitrogen, phosphorus and potassium (N, P, K).

Gardeners and farmers know that if they are going to grow the many different plants we eat and enjoy successfully, they need to add fertiliser to the soil. This provides the plants with all of the nutrients they need for healthy growth. Fertilisers often show the percentages of these three minerals on the front label of the bag like the one in Figure 6.

Figure 6   The percentages of N, P and K in this bag of fertiliser are shown on the bag.

Gardeners and farmers know that the minerals are always listed in the order N then P then K.

- Nitrogen (N) is the main nutrient needed by plants for new, green plant growth. Plants that are mainly leaves (such as grass) need plenty of nitrogen, so the first number is very high in fertilisers for lawns.

- Phosphorus (P) helps the plant grow roots. It also increases the numbers of flowers on flowering plants. Lots of phosphorus is very useful for plants that have bulbs and for newly-planted trees and shrubs. Fertilisers for these plants often have high middle numbers.

- Potassium (K) is good for the overall health of plants. It helps them withstand very hot or cold weather and helps to defend them against diseases. Most soils already have some potassium, so the third number in the fertiliser may be smaller than the other two.

Plants also need small amounts of other minerals for healthy growth, such as calcium (Ca) to improve the growth of young roots and shoots and magnesium (Mg) to help seed formation. Magnesium is also an important part of the chemical chlorophyll. Finally sulphur (S) and iron (Fe) help the plant to maintain a dark green colour.

Minerals and nutrients are not the only factors that affect the growth of plants. Some plants are affected by the pH of the soil they grow in.

Killing weeds

Just like animals, plants compete for natural resources, such as space, light, water and nutrients. Farmers and gardeners have to deal with the problem of weeds competing with their plants or crops. Herbicides have been developed to combat this problem.

When plants are grown, they all have to compete for space, light, water and nutrients. If you look at a packet of seeds the instructions normally tell you how far apart the seeds should be planted. This makes sure that when the plants are fully-grown, they are not competing for valuable resources. Farmers have to plant their crops very carefully to make sure that the crop they grow gives the biggest harvest and the healthiest plants.

Weeds

A weed is any plant that grows where we don't want it. Weeds are a serious threat to our food crops so farmers often use **herbicides**.

Herbicides can be used to control weeds. Some herbicides kill parts of the plant that they come into contact with, other herbicides are absorbed either by the roots or leaves of the plant and then move within the plant slowly killing it.

Non-selective herbicides – which kill a wide range of plants – can only be used before the crop starts to grow. Once the crop appears above the surface of the soil, **selective herbicides** that only kill certain types of weeds have to be used.

1 General herbicide application

This method uses a crop sprayer to spray the whole of a field or an area of it. The crop sprayer may be a large self-propelled machine with a wide boom carrying the spray nozzles, a tractor-mounted machine, or a sprayer mounted on an 'all terrain vehicle' (ATV or quad bike). The spray will be a selective herbicide.

2 Spot application

This method uses a small sprayer carried on the person's back, with a hand pump. Individual weeds or patches of weeds, such as thistles or docks, may be sprayed by this method. The benefits of this method are that it may be suitable for controlling the occasional small patch of weeds.

3 The weed wiper

This method uses a wick soaked in herbicide, mounted on a short boom trailed behind a tractor or ATV. The height of the boom is controlled to only allow taller plants to come into contact with the wick. This can be particularly useful for controlling tall weeds such as thistles, docks and nettles.

It is really only in the last 50 years that we have used herbicides to control weeds. Before this, we either had to pull out the weeds by hand, plough them into the soil or sort out the seeds to prevent the weeds being planted with the crops. Herbicides are also used extensively on industrial sites, roadsides, ditches, banks and recreational areas.

Pests

In biology, a pest is any animal that will destroy crops. Anything from field mice to cabbage white butterflies to aphids, slugs and snails are pests. Farmers and gardeners need to control them in much the same way as they need to control weeds, though there are more options available. Since the 1970s, farmers have been using more and more herbicides, pesticides and fungicides to control the damage that pests do to their crops, rather than using organic methods. Organic methods of pest control include the use of other insects as predators that feed off the pests and not the crops. The use of chemicals has reduced the populations of birds that rely on those same pests and plants as food.

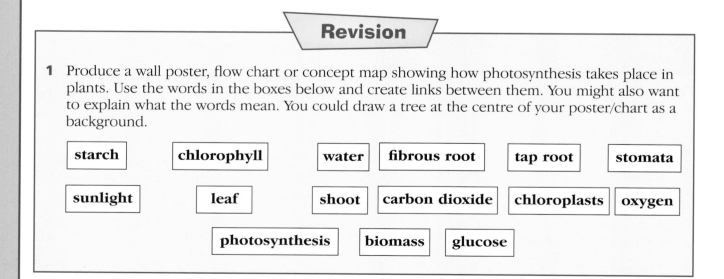

Revision

1 Produce a wall poster, flow chart or concept map showing how photosynthesis takes place in plants. Use the words in the boxes below and create links between them. You might also want to explain what the words mean. You could draw a tree at the centre of your poster/chart as a background.

| starch | chlorophyll | water | fibrous root | tap root | stomata |

| sunlight | leaf | shoot | carbon dioxide | chloroplasts | oxygen |

| photosynthesis | biomass | glucose |

Revision

2 Put the following sentences into a sensible order.

- Killing the weeds can also affect other plants and animals in the food web.

- These chemicals are called herbicides.

- Just like animals, plants have to compete for natural resources, such as light, water, nutrients and space.

- Weeds, like all other plants, are often part of a food web.

- Some herbicides are general and will kill any plants that grow in a field.

- Farmers need to control weeds to make sure that the crops they grow are not competing for resources with the weeds.

- Farmers and gardeners often use chemicals to control the growth of weeds.

- Plants that grow where they are not wanted are called weeds.

- Other herbicides are selective and kill just the weeds.

Questions

1 The word equation for respiration is:

oxygen + glucose → carbon + water + energy
dioxide

The word equation for photosynthesis is:

sunlight
carbon dioxide + water → glucose + oxygen
chlorophyll

In what ways are they similar and in what ways are they different?

2 Grass has fibrous roots and no tap roots. How does having a fibrous root system help the grass in fields of sheep and cows?

3 How can a tap root help trees in hot countries such as Greece where they have little to no rain and strong winds called the meltemi during July and August?

Use the graphs on page 49 to answer questions 4–9. Explain how the shape of the graphs helps you find the answer.

4 What is the best temperature to keep plants at if you want them to photosynthesise?

5 What happens to the rate of photosynthesis after about 40°C?

6 Describe what happens to the rate of photosynthesis if you increase the level of carbon dioxide.

7 Can you just keep increasing the amount of light to make the plant photosynthesise more? Explain your answer.

8 If a plant is given plenty of carbon dioxide, will it just keep on making more and more sugar? Explain your answer.

9 Describe what happens when the light intensity increases.

10 A cactus is a plant with no leaves. Where does a cactus make its food and where does it store its supplies of food and water?

11 If a large, heavy, tall tree had a fibrous root system instead of a tap root, what problems or advantages might it have in the following situations:

a) a long dry summer

b) a winter with lots of rain

c) a sudden period of gale force winds?

Particles

4.1 Changes

Key Words

melting	pressure
freezing	density
condensing	expansion
boiling	anomalous
evaporating	Brownian motion
states of matter	
diffusion	
kinetic theory of matter	

The Carnival model is just a way to think about how particles move.

Carnival people

All matter is made of tiny particles. They move about constantly, even in solids.

Solid, liquid and gas are the three **states of matter.** They are very different because of the way the particles move about and how they are packed together.

The particles are tiny – far too small to see and all the particles are moving all the time.

The particles in a **solid** are like the person in the stands (Figure 2). Each person has a fixed place. The people have no spaces between them. They are all in neat rows.

The people can move about a little, but they do not move out of their place. The block always stays the same shape.

Figure 1 Carnival at Sambadrome

Figure 2 Watching the carnival from the stands

The people standing in the crowd are like the particles in a **liquid** (Figure 3). They are all pushed together but they are in a jumble. The people can move past each other. Like the particles in a liquid they will take the shape of the 'container'.

Gas particles are like the people dancing (Figure 4). They are all moving about very quickly and often bump in to each other. Gases mix easily with each other – that is how a smell spreads through the air – the smell is carried by a gas. This is called **diffusion**.

All the particles in solids, liquids and gases have energy. The particles are moving all the time, even in solids. This idea of particles moving is called the **kinetic theory of matter**.

Figure 3   Standing in the crowd at the carnival

If you make the people in the stands more excited – then they move about more. This is like making a solid more 'excited' by giving it extra energy. This makes its temperature higher and its particles vibrate faster.

The carnival procession could go through a narrower space if it needed to. This is like squashing a gas. Gases are easy to compress, and they diffuse and mix.

Figure 4   Dancers at the carnival

Hardness

Some materials are easy to cut and some are hard.

Wood and plastic are easier to cut than metal. This is because the forces between particles are stronger in metals than in wood and plastic. Some wood can be pulled apart into fibres. The forces holding the wood particles together within a fibre are stronger than those holding one fibre to another.

Soft materials like wax, Plasticine and clay have particles that hold on to each other very weakly, so they can be easily squashed into a new shape.

Density

Metals are most often 'heavier for their size' than other materials. This is because the metal particles are each heavier than the particles in wood and plastic.

The property 'heaviness for its size' has a proper name. It is called **density**. Density is measured in g/cm^3. This is how many grams each centimetre cube of the material weighs. Often density is measured in kg/m^3, this is how many kilograms a metre cube of the material weights.

Remember:
density equals mass
divided by volume.

Hodder Science Summary Book

Expansion

Figure 5   Expansion joint of a bridge

> Expansion can cause huge forces that crack strong materials.

Motorway bridges, like the one in Figure 5, are solid slabs. On a hot summer day they expand, increasing in length. This causes problems due to the enormous force the expansion causes. This could buckle and crack the bridge so there have to be special sliding joints to help cope with those forces.

Another example of expansion is seen in thermometers. When the liquid in a thermometer gets hotter, it expands up the narrow tube above the bulb. Because the tube is narrow, a small change in temperature and a small expansion of the liquid makes a big difference to the level in the tube.

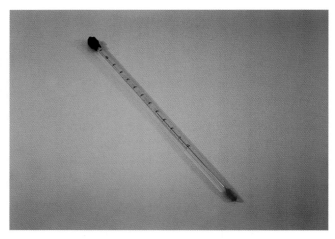

Figure 6   A simple thermometer

When air is hot it expands a great deal. This makes it lighter for its size (i.e. less dense) than the normal air around it. Because it is less dense, it will float up in the normal air.

Figure 7   A gathering of hot air balloons

Ice is the odd one out

Nearly all solids expand when they melt. But the ice/water change is different.

Ice cubes float in a glass of water. They must be less heavy for their size than the water around them. Water must expand when it freezes.

Figure 8 The metal pipe has cracked due to water expanding on freezing.

Stretchy and bendy

The arrangement of particles in solids helps us explain why different materials are used for different purposes.

If the fillings in Figure 9 were harder than the tooth enamel, they would damage the surrounding teeth. Dentists often use gold to replace teeth because it has the right hardness.

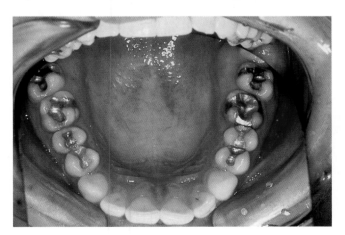

Figure 9 Fillings are not as hard as tooth enamel.

Wood is flexible. This is because the particles in wood are long and thin and bend without breaking.

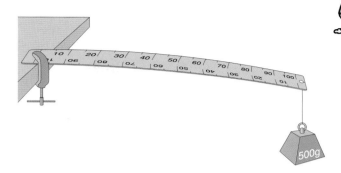

Figure 10 Wood is flexible

Rubber is stretchy. The particles in rubber are folded up like a zigzag. When the rubber is pulled, the zigzag particles straighten out without breaking.

Figure 11 A stretchy rubber band

Hitting the water

Particles in a liquid are like the pattern in a children's ball pond.

The particles are close together but in a jumble.

Figure 12 Children playing in a ball pond

Step into the ball pond and you can sink right through it. Your legs feel no resistance as they push the particles apart. The ball pond will take the shape of whatever room or space it is in.

A soft landing

A crash mat is full of air, and slows the pole-vaulter down to a soft landing.

> Gases are squashy. The particles can be pushed closer together unlike solids or liquids.

Figure 13   A pole-vaulter from 1933 (top). A modern pole-vaulter (bottom).

Always moving and mixing

Figure 14   The crowd at the carnival take the shape of the space behind the barrier.

Liquids fill up whatever shape of space there is (Figure 14). But the particles do not stand still. They move past each other freely even though they are packed close together.

Figure 15   The dancers spread out into the space available.

Gases flow, but the particles are far apart and are moving quickly. Gases spread to take up all the space in whatever container they are in (Figure 15). The gas particles move about everywhere sometimes bumping into each other or bouncing back from the walls. The force of them bumping into the walls creates pressure.

Revision

1 Make a list of 20 things you have breathed, eaten or used today. Next to each thing write if it is a solid, liquid or gas.

2 Imagine you are a video director making a film to explain the properties of solids, liquids and gases to junior school pupils. Make a storyboard of the scenes you would set up, with real carnival dancers to show the properties. Create scenes that show melting, boiling, condensing, freezing and diffusion. Make a scene that shows the difference between evaporation (from the surface) and boiling (from the whole bulk of the liquid).

Questions

Use the 'carnival people' model to answer questions 1 to 8.

1 Draw a picture of the people in the stands. The seats are so close together that their shoulders touch and their knees are against the shoulders of the people below them.

2 Imagine you are in the stands at the carnival. Explain how you could move a little without leaving your seat.

3 Draw a picture of the people in the crowd as a random jumble of people.

4 Write about when you have been in crowds that are packed tightly together. Explain how you were able to move.

5 A gas would be like people running round in the school hall. Draw a picture of this.

6 What would make the people in your picture from question 5 change direction?

7 What would be the difference to your picture from question 5 if the people were running round on the school field?

8 What would happen if lots of people in the hall were running into the doors?

9 A saw to cut wood is made of metal. Explain how you can tell that wood particles are held together less strongly than particles in metals?

10 If you threw a key and a wooden desk into a river, only the desk would float. Why?

11 When clothes are repaired, the 'stretch-iness' of the repair material has to be the same as that of the cloth. Explain why.

12 Draw a strip cartoon showing a belly flop into a ball pond. Add speech bubbles to it. Explain what has happened using scientific words.

13 Sabash helps at his uncle's shop. They put a bowl of water outside for the customers' dogs to drink. On summer days the bowl needs filling several times a day as the water vanishes. The family disagrees about the reasons for this.

Uncle: There are more customers in the summer and some are clumsy and kick the bowl.

Cousin: There is more wind and this evaporates the water.

Aunt: There are more people taking dogs for a walk.

Sabash: It's hotter in summer, so the water evaporates faster.

a) What sort of statements are the family making?

b) Sabash is sure he is right. He decides to use a ruler to measure the depth of the water in the bowl. But he knows the investigation needs careful planning.

Write a full plan for Sabash's investigation. Include:

- how he would make it a fair test by controlling other factors;

- a table of results for him to fill in for the 6 hours he is helping in the shop.

4.2 Solutions

Key Words

solute
solvent
solution
concentrated
saturated
crystallisation

distillation
fractional distillation
chromatography
fermentation

Good solutions

A solute dissolves in a solvent to make a solution.

When substances dissolve, the **solution** is transparent (see-through). If it is not transparent, it is not a real solution. These non-transparent liquids are called **suspensions**.

Figure 1 Tom is in trouble at the café. He forgot to filter the coffee!

To make coffee you need to pour boiling water on to the ground coffee. You then filter the liquid and the boiling water dissolves the coffee taste out of the ground up coffee and the rest stays in the filter paper. To make a strong (or concentrated) coffee you need to use a lot of ground coffee.

A **concentrated solution** has more **solute** (dissolved solid) in the **solvent** (liquid that does the dissolving).

Dissolving needs a solute and a solvent – melting just needs one substance.

Picture solutions

A solution does not have the same properties as a pure substance.

Figure 2 You must develop and fix film photos.

When a photograph is taken you must take the film out of the camera and develop it. You must dilute the chemicals to the correct **concentration**. If the image gets too dark, the picture will be ruined.

The fixer solution, which stops the picture getting too dark, needs changing every day, not because the chemicals have been used up, but because the solution becomes **saturated** with material out of the film.

Complete solutions

A solution forms in the following way:

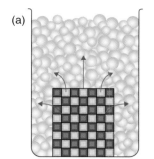

Key
- Water particles
- Salt particles

The solvent particles break the forces between the particles of the solid and pull it apart.

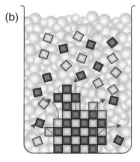

The solid gets dissolved layer by layer from the outside in.

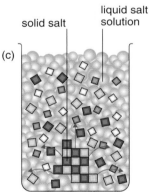

solid salt   liquid salt solution

The solid gets split up into tiny particles and cannot be seen.

Figure 3   Forming a salt water solution

A concentrated solution has lots of solute particles in a certain volume. A dilute solution has few dissolved particles in a certain volume.

Unscrambling liquids

Methods that separate solutes from solvents include crystallising, distilling, evaporating and chromatography.

Salt from sea water

Table salt is the chemical **sodium chloride**. To get salt from sea water the water is pumped into a pond and left to **evaporate** in the Sun. The solution becomes more concentrated as the water evaporates. Another substance called **calcium sulphate** comes out of this concentrated solution of sea water as a solid. This process is called **crystallising**. The calcium sulphate tastes nasty so is separated out and the concentrated solution is pumped to a second pond. Here the sodium chloride crystallises out. The sodium chloride (table salt) is dried in the Sun for people to use.

Desalination

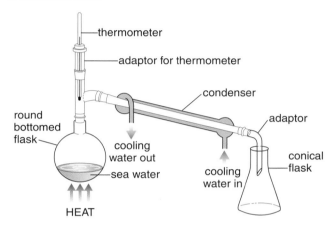

Figure 4   How to distil water in the laboratory

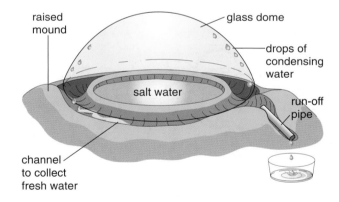

Figure 5   Making pure water by distillation

In a dry country, a simple glass dome over a pool of salt water will make pure water. The Sun evaporates the water. The vapour then condenses in the dome. This process is called **distillation**.

Chromatography

In Figure 6 the solvent soaks up through the paper carrying the ink (which was a dot on the paper) with it. The solvent carries the more soluble dyes up the paper faster than the less soluble ones. This is called **chromatography**.

Figure 6   Separating the colours in ink by chromatography

States change

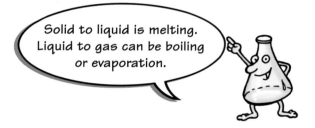

Solid to liquid is melting. Liquid to gas can be boiling or evaporation.

Figure 7   Melting chocolate

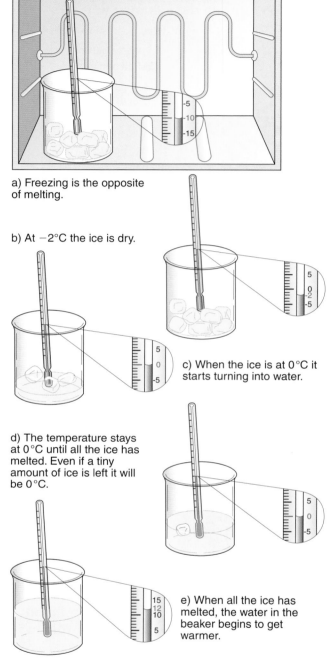

a) Freezing is the opposite of melting.

b) At −2°C the ice is dry.

c) When the ice is at 0°C it starts turning into water.

d) The temperature stays at 0°C until all the ice has melted. Even if a tiny amount of ice is left it will be 0°C.

e) When all the ice has melted, the water in the beaker begins to get warmer.

Figure 8

When a cook melts chocolate, it changes from being chunks of solid chocolate to a thick liquid. It has to be heated for this to happen.

When melted chocolate is spread on a cake it solidifies as it cools. It remains in the spread shape. A 250 g bar of solid milk chocolate makes 250 g of melted chocolate.

Boiling

Hot chocolate needs hot milk. When you heat milk it gains energy.

When it begins to boil, the milk forms lots of bubbles because the liquid milk turns into a gas. The frothy milk will spill out of the pan if you don't stop heating. The gas takes up more room than the liquid.

Gases and boiling

There are some important things to remember about gases and boiling:

- When a liquid boils it becomes a very large volume of gas.

- Mixtures of liquids can be separated by distillation.

- Solutions do not have the same boiling point as pure liquids.

Fractional distillation

Figure 9   An 'Alcool' station in Brazil

In Brazil lots of sugar cane is grown. This can be used to make a fuel for motor cars. The sugar is **fermented**, like when beer and wine are made. This turns most of the sugar into a chemical called **ethanol**.

Fermentation creates a mixture of ethanol, water and yeast. This is useless as a fuel. **Fractional distillation** can be used to separate the mixture of **liquids** because they boil at different temperatures. Ethanol boils at a lower temperature than water so it vaporises first when the mixture is heated. This vapour is condensed to give a fuel that is nearly pure ethanol.

At the cold end of the scale

You can also turn a gas into a liquid just by compressing it, i.e. squeezing it into a smaller space. The particles get pushed closer and closer together until they are touching. This is how liquid air is made.

Liquid air is very cold. The different substances in air can then be separated by distillation when the air warms up because they have different boiling points.

Gas	Boiling point °C
oxygen	−183
argon	−186
nitrogen	−196

Boiling

Liquid particles are in contact mostly because of **air pressure** pushing down on them.

To turn into a gas the **particles** need to move faster. Energy makes them move faster.

You can see the steam rising from the surface of hot water as just a few water particles escape. At 100 °C, all the particles are moving fast enough to escape. Large holes appear in the liquid and the water boils.

Revision

1   You know a lot about solutions and dissolving from earlier years. Make a simple concept map linking these words.

**water   sugar   salt   dissolving
solution   high temperature
small lumps   speed of dissolving**

Now add the ideas/words, below, into your concept map. Write these words on cards or pieces of paper and move them to see where they fit best.

**solvent   solute   saturated
concentrated   crystallisation
distillation**

2   Write the meanings of the words above on the back of the cards.

Questions

1 Your small sister has mixed tiny glass beads with sugar. How could you get the beads back using water?

2 If you make a thermos flask of instant coffee, you need to use much more coffee powder than you would for just a mugful. Explain why.

3 Draw particle pictures of strong and weak solutions. If it was a coloured solute, how would the colours of the solutions be different?

4 Devise a test to find out how much salt will dissolve in 100 cm³ of cold water. Write step-by-step instructions.

5 If you dive too deep or come up too quickly, your blood becomes like a shaken can of cola. Explain why this happens remembering that gases such as nitrogen and oxygen are dissolved in the blood.

Use the following information to answer questions 6 to 10:

Sugar comes from sugar cane that grows in tropical countries. The sugar is extracted by shredding up the sugar cane and mixing it with hot water to make a sugary solution. This solution is then evaporated to make a saturated solution. The sugar crystallises out from this.

6 What conditions does sugar need to grow?

7 Why is the cane shredded before the juice is extracted?

8 Why is hot water used?

9 What is crystallisation?

10 Draw a particle picture of a saturated sugar solution.

11 Write step-by-step instructions to tell someone how to make pure water from sea water.

12 'Black ink is actually made from several different coloured inks.'

Explain how you could try to prove this was true.

13 Draw a strip cartoon of what an ice cube would look like as it melts.

14 Why does water boil at a higher temperature in a pressure cooker? Explain by writing about the speed of the particles.

15 Copy and complete the word grid using these clues.

a) Small pieces of a liquid

b) The solution you write with

c) The solid that dissolves

d) The liquid that does the dissolving

e) When a solution dries out the solvent . . .

f) The mixture of dissolved solid and liquid

g) A solution for treating wood

h) The meaning of transparent

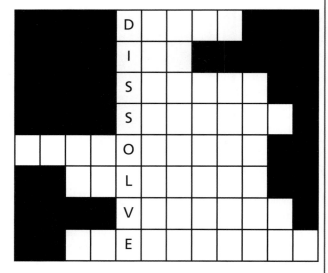

16 Draw a bar chart to display the solubility of the pure substances below.

Substance	Table salt	Fungus killer (blue)	Washing soda	Drain clearer	Fertiliser
Mass dissolved in 100 g of water at 20 °C	36 g	122 g	21 g	109 g	122 g

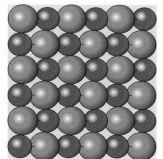

4.3 Building blocks

Key Words	
pure substance	protons
material	neutrons
atom	electrons
molecule	metal
element	non-metal
compound	conducts energy
Periodic Table	malleable
atomic number	ductile
mass number	

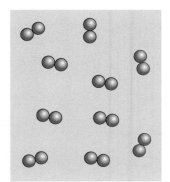

Atoms are the smallest particles that exist on their own in the ordinary material around us.

Elements, mixtures and compounds

Mixtures are things that can be separated into different pure substances, for example salt water is a mixture. Pure substances are a much harder idea to understand.

Pure substances are those where all the particles

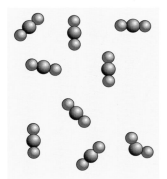

Figure 1 Oxygen (left) is an element. It contains only oxygen atoms, but the atoms 'go round in pairs' to make oxygen molecules. Carbon dioxide (right) contains carbon atoms and oxygen atoms so it is a compound. All carbon dioxide molecules contain one carbon atom joined to two oxygen atoms.

are exactly the same. They can be divided into two types:

- Elements are pure substances where all the atoms are the same type.

- Compounds are pure substances where different atoms have joined together to make molecules.

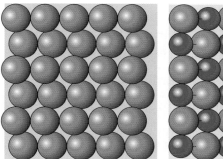

Figure 2 Copper (left) is an element. The copper atoms are in a regular pattern because it is a solid. Copper oxide (right) is a compound. There is one oxygen atom joined to every copper atom.

Elements

All the atoms in an element are the same type.

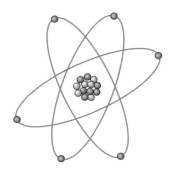

Figure 3 An atom

One hundred million atoms in a line would fit into 1 cm.

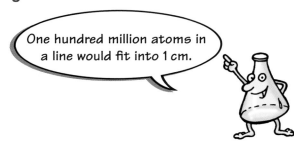

Atoms are made of smaller particles called **protons**, **neutrons** and **electrons**. The outer part is made up of electrons. Atoms are fuzzy at the edges; they tend to stick together by sharing their electrons.

Hodder Science Summary Book

Metals

Most elements are metals, a few are non-metals. There are about 70 metallic elements.

Metals all share certain properties:

- they are shiny, if the surface is clean
- they make a nice 'ting' if hit
- they are tough
- they do not shatter
- they can be shaped by bending them
- they do not crack easily
- they can hold large weights without breaking
- most metals don't melt easily – only one metal (mercury) is a liquid
- some metals are magnetic
- they conduct energy easily
- they conduct electricity well.

Metals are very useful materials. They are the only solid materials that transfer energy easily by conduction.

Testing for metals – conduction

If the solid material being tested is put into a circuit and conducts electricity, it is a metal. Also, if it is a metal, it continues to feel cold to your hand.

Metal surfaces combine with oxygen in the air. This can make the surface go dull. With iron and steel this corrosion is called rusting.

Non-metals

There are only about 20 elements that are non-metals:

- many are gases
- the ones that aren't gases all have low melting points
- they are brittle if they are solid
- they do not conduct energy well
- they do not conduct electricity.

Very few of the non-metals are useful materials.

The **Periodic Table** (Figure 4) is a list of all the elements we know. It is a list in order of **atomic number**, and groups similar elements together. There are just over 100 elements, but only 90 of these are found naturally in the Earth's crust.

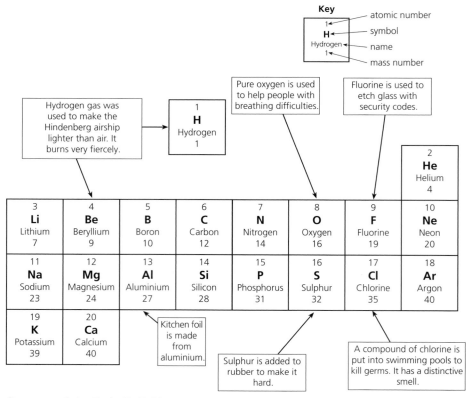

Figure 4   The first part of the Periodic Table

Example	Metal	Example of use	Useful property
	gold	jewellery	it stays shiny
	iron	bridges	it is very strong
	copper	electric cables	it conducts electricity well and is flexible
	brass	electric plugs and switches	it conducts electricity well and is hard
	stainless steel	saucepans	it is strong even when thin and conducts heat well
	aluminium	kitchen foil	it is flexible and can be rolled out into thin sheets

Table 1 Some metals and their uses

Making compounds

Elements can react together to make new compounds. These compounds are still pure substances. They contain a fixed ratio of atoms from the elements that made them.

Atoms join together in different ways to form compounds. In compounds the clusters of atoms are called molecules. Each molecule is exactly the same.

- For metal atoms to form a compound, they have to combine with non-metal atoms.

- Non-metal atoms can combine together in groups to make compounds.

- Molecules usually contain small numbers of

atoms. Carbon atoms are the exception to this. They can make large complex molecules.

- When new molecules are formed, the atoms don't vanish, they just get rearranged.

New rock

When cement is mixed with sand and water it sets really hard. It doesn't just dry out, it changes chemically to a new substance.

Calcium oxide in the cement absorbs carbon dioxide from the air. Mixing it with water helps this process. Hard calcium carbonate crystals are formed.

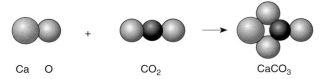

Ca   O CO_2 $CaCO_3$

Figure 5   The reaction to produce calcium carbonate

Figure 6   a) Calcium oxide coming out of the cement kiln. b) It gets mixed with water, sand and gravel. c) The mix gets smoothed into a path and carbon dioxide molecules gradually disappear into the path.

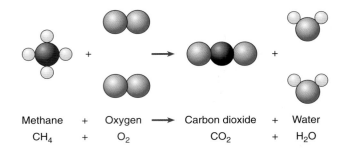

Methane   +   Oxygen   ⟶   Carbon dioxide   +   Water
CH_4 + O_2 CO_2 + H_2O

Figure 7   The atoms involved in the reaction between methane and oxygen

Burning methane

When methane burns in oxygen, the hydrogen atoms get pinched first from the methane molecule to make water molecules.
Then the carbon atoms in the methane combine with oxygen to make carbon dioxide gas.

Revision

1   Make a set of Key Word file cards. Put one word from the Key Words list at the beginning of this section on each card and write the meaning of that word underneath. Then write a sentence including that word, to show its meaning. Swap your set of file cards with a partner and check each other's set. Suggest improvements if some of the sentences are not clear.

2   First, make an A–Z list of the names or symbols of the elements without looking at a copy of the Periodic Table. Then fill in the gaps using a Periodic Table. Work with a partner. See if you can each make different lists. Don't bother with Q or J, but make sure you include W as it is a symbol for an element.

Questions

1 Both melting and dissolving make liquids. Explain the difference between the two words.

2 Distillation is a way of making very pure water for an experiment. Explain what happens when water is distilled.

3 Explain each of these terms:

  a) atom

  b) element

  c) compound

  d) molecule.

4 Water molecules have two hydrogen atoms and one oxygen atom. Draw a particle picture of water vapour.

5 Draw a big particle picture of air. Air contains oxygen molecules, nitrogen molecules, argon atoms and carbon dioxide molecules.

6 Name five elements shown in the Periodic Table that are gases.

7 Name five elements shown in the Periodic Table that are metals.

8 What is the name of the element with the same atomic number as your age?

9 Which metals are magnetic?

10 Rearrange the table below. Match the correct property to the metal.

Metal	Property
copper	very hard, used for aeroplane parts
gold	very light, used for window frames
aluminium	stays shiny, used for jewellery
titanium	liquid metal, used in thermometers
mercury	conducts electricity well, used for wires

11 Rearrange the table below. Match the non-metallic elements with their uses in the table below.

Non-metallic element	Use
carbon	very light gas, used in balloons
chlorine	gas we use in our bodies which is taken in by the lungs
helium	barbecue charcoal; burns well to give lots of heat
oxygen	kills germs in water supply and swimming pools

12 In equations, water molecules are written as H_2O and methane molecules as CH_4. This is called their formula. Explain why they are written like this.

13 Describe how you could test a material to see if it was a metal or a non-metal.

14 Draw a cartoon strip of a steel bucket as it gradually rusts away. Explain what is happening.

15 Celia took the temperature of a small amount of salol as it cooled.

Here are her results.

Time (mins)	0	1	2	3	4	5
Temp (°C)	70	60	50	44	46	46
Time (mins)	6	7	8	9	10	
Temp (°C)	46	40	34	28	23	

  a) Plot a graph of her results.

  b) What state was salol in at the start of the experiment (solid, liquid or gas)?

  c) What state was salol in at the end of the experiment (solid, liquid or gas)?

  d) What was the melting point of salol?

4.4 Reactions and mixtures

Key Words

Key Words

distillation   precipitation
alloy   displacement
oxidation   enzyme
reduction   combining power
thermal decomposition

Pure substances

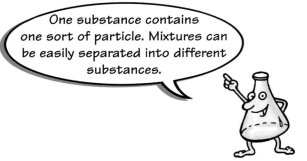

> One substance contains one sort of particle. Mixtures can be easily separated into different substances.

To most people a pure substance means one that contains no harmful substances. In science, pure means containing only one type of particle.

These are pure substances:

● pure water – contains only water particles

● copper metal – contains only copper particles

● sugar crystals – contain only sugar particles

Really pure water is called distilled water. This water has been evaporated and condensed, leaving all the dissolved substances behind. In real life we use very few really pure substances. Most materials have better properties if they are a mixture.

Figure 1   This is what you need to make a cup of white coffee and a sponge cake.

Mixtures

Nearly all the cooking we do makes mixtures. Mixtures can make very useful materials. They often have very different properties from the pure substances that make them.

Figure 2   Coal burns and disappears?

Air

Air is a mixture and not a pure substance.

In many chemical changes the substances seem to gain or lose mass. In fact the mass is being transferred to and from a store of materials in the air.

Many things use air as a raw material (see Table 2).

Strange reactions

There are many different types of chemical reactions and changes. Chemical changes are predictable – they always happen the same way.

Oxidation

When you heat most metals they react with the oxygen in the air. They make new substances called oxides.

Combustion

Combustion is a special sort of oxidation reaction. Oxygen in the air is used to burn a fuel and transfer energy causing heating.

Thermal decomposition

Lots of substances decompose when heated. Making toffee is a decomposition reaction. When you heat sugar, some of the particles fall apart to make 'caramel', so you get a nice texture and stronger taste.

Precipitation

When you bubble carbon dioxide gas through lime water solution they react and an insoluble substance is made. The insoluble substance makes the liquid cloudy.

Displacement

Titanium ore is turned into metal by using sodium. The sodium steals, or displaces, the oxygen from the titanium ore, leaving only useful titanium metal.

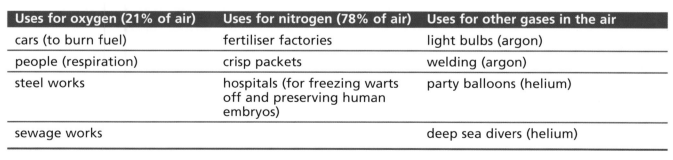

Chemical reactions just rearrange the atoms into different substances.

Uses for oxygen (21% of air)	Uses for nitrogen (78% of air)	Uses for other gases in the air
cars (to burn fuel)	fertiliser factories	light bulbs (argon)
people (respiration)	crisp packets	welding (argon)
steel works	hospitals (for freezing warts off and preserving human embryos)	party balloons (helium)
sewage works		deep sea divers (helium)

Table 2   Uses of the components of air

Fizz reactions

Figure 3 A fizz reaction

Figure 3 shows sulphuric acid and sodium hydrogen carbonate being mixed. This reaction makes lots of fizz as carbon dioxide gas is given off.

Enzyme reactions
Enzymes break up big complicated particles into small simpler substances.

Neutralising acids
Acid nettle sting is neutralised by an alkaline dock leaf. The dock leaf is not harmful to us as it is only a weak alkali.

It's frighteningly tiny

This section is a thinking model to help you understand how atoms join together.

When you were small you felt safe if your hands were held. Atoms are the same. They are 'safe' if all their hands are being held. But atoms have different numbers of hands, i.e. they have different valency.

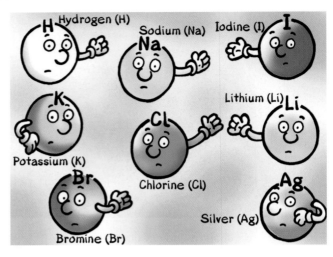

Figure 4 These atoms have one hand (or a valency of 1).

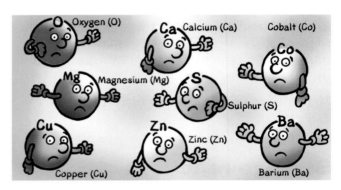

Figure 5 These atoms have two hands (or a valency of 2).

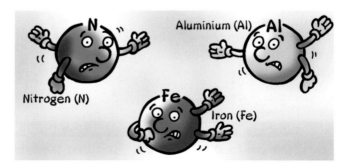

Figure 6 These atoms have three hands (or a valency of 3).

Figure 7 This atom has four hands (or a valency of 4).

When atoms hold hands with their friends they are happy.

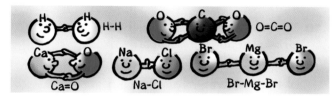

Figure 8 Atoms join to form molecules.

They have reacted. They are safe from change for a while.

This group is a molecule. It has no free hands so it cannot react any more.

There are some 'dead tough' atoms. They stay on their own all the time. They form no compounds at all.

Figure 9 These atoms do not form compounds.

Of course, this is only a story to help you understand. The number of hands is called the valency. Make sure you know the number of 'hands for each atom'.

Always the same recipe

Cooking and chemistry both have very precise rules – follow them correctly and the results are predictable.

Cooks make perfect cakes every time. They combine exactly the right quantities of different ingredients so they react with each other completely.

When chemicals react, they follow rules about how much of one element will combine with another and what the compound will be like. Even when chemicals fall apart, they do it according to the same sort of strict rules.

Three oxygen particles combine with six lithium particles to make three lithium oxides.

Six oxygen particles combine with 12 lithium particles to make six lithium oxides.

One copper carbonate splits up into one copper oxide and one carbon dioxide molecule.

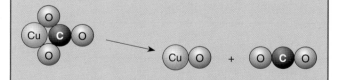

Five copper carbonates split up into five copper oxides and five carbon dioxide molecules.

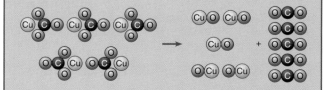

Questions

Use the particle pictures to answer questions 1–9.

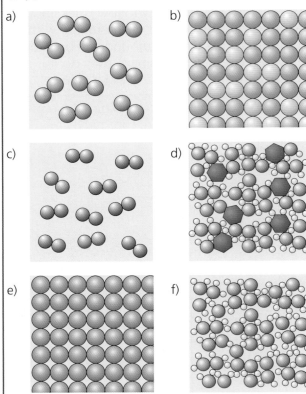

a) b)

c) d)

e) f)

Look at the six boxes in the diagram above.

1 Which two are gases?

2 Which is pure oxygen?

3 Which is air (oxygen and other gases mixed)?

4 Which two are liquids?

5 Which is pure water and which is sugar dissolved in water?

6 Draw a diagram to show the particles in pure solid sugar.

7 Which two diagrams show solid materials?

8 One is pure copper metal, the other is brass (a mixture of copper and zinc metals). Which is pure copper and which is brass?

9 Draw a diagram to show what the particles in pure zinc metal would be like.

10 The air we breathe out is heavier than the air we breathe in. Explain why.

11 What type of reaction is happening in each of the following? Explain your answers.

a) Charcoal is made by heating wood.

b) Acid indigestion is treated with alkaline tablets.

c) Petrol burns in a car engine to release heat.

d) Milk goes sour as it reacts with the air.

e) Limestone rock makes bubbles when vinegar is put on it.

f) Vinegar is used to ease the pain of a wasp sting.

g) Washing soda produces an insoluble scum in hard water areas.

h) Copper metal gets deposited on the surface of an iron knife; iron particles take the place of the copper in the solution.

Revision

1 Work with two other people. Make a set of ten questions each. Make the questions contain these words:

pure substances gases in the air oxygen oxides combustion

oxidisation and reduction thermal decomposition precipitation displacement

enzyme reaction neutralisation

Then take it in turns to ask your partners to answer your questions. Each person will have ten questions to ask and 20 to answer. See who scores the most.

2 Use the 'particle people' pictures to draw particles for different compounds. Make a display of these.

Reactions

5.1 Acids, alkalis and salts

Key Words

acid	indicator
alkali	pH scale
salt	hydrogen ion
sour	hydroxide ion
soapy	neutralisation
corrosive	indigestion
hazardous	

Chemical opposites

You have seen bottles of acid. They have the corrosive symbol on them.

Acids are not all dangerous. Lemons, milk and 'sour ball' sweets are acids.

You have heard of alkalis. These are the chemical opposite of acids. But beware, they can be just as dangerous as acids. Alkalis taste very nasty – just like soap.

Acids and alkalis react with each other. They cancel each other out and make new substances. These new substances are salts.

All acids react in a similar way. All acids change the colour of indicators. Litmus is a coloured dye that comes from plants. Acids change litmus to a red colour and alkalis make litmus blue.

Using acids

- Metal cleaner: acid particles dissolve the dull oxide layer.

- Vitamin C: this is added to food so that the acid particles gobble up the oxygen particles that make food go off.

- Acid in aspirin attacks harmful particles in our blood.

Figure 1 Acid particles behave like these nippy mice.

Acid particles are like mice. They are nippy particles that move about 'biting' others and making them change. Like mice, a few acid particles are not a problem – they can even be quite useful and nice. But when there are lots and lots they become dangerous.

Using alkalis

Alkalis are often used to destroy grease. Oven cleaner is a strong alkali. Alkali particles do not taste nice at all. That's why toothpaste and indigestion tablets always have a strong flavour added.

Measuring acids

Universal Indicator is a mixture of dyes that goes different colours according to how concentrated the acid or alkali in a solution is.

The pH scale is a scale for measuring acidity. You can get the pH number by looking at the colour that Universal Indicator turns and matching it (Figure 2).

Less dangerous acids

citric acid – lemonade

malic acid – apples

tartaric acid – baking powder

ethanoic acid – vinegar

More dangerous laboratory acids

sulphuric acid – car batteries

nitric acid – cleaning metals

hydrochloric acid – there is a weak solution of hydrochloric acid in the stomach

Table 1   Common acids and where they are found

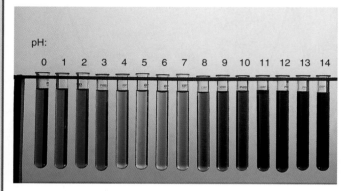

Figure 2   The colour range of Universal Indicator. The pH number shown by each colour is given above the tubes.

Figure 3   The 'savage' hydrogen and hydroxide ions.

Why are acids dangerous?

Acids dissolve and split up to make smaller particles. Some of these particles are hydrogen ions. They are like fierce animals – they will tear other particles apart.

The hydrogen ion particles react with metals and rocks. They can also destroy your skin and leave your flesh exposed. Lots of acid particles are a problem but your tough skin can cope with a few acid particles. They will even tickle your taste buds (like in lemonade).

Alkali substances dissolve to make hydroxide ions. They are as fierce as hydrogen ions in acids. They will attack grease in your skin, flesh and even wood. They are called caustic chemicals.

Salt and water

There are many different sorts of salts.

Acids and alkalis neutralise each other. Water molecules get made in the reaction. The bits left over make a **salt**.

acid + alkali → salt + water

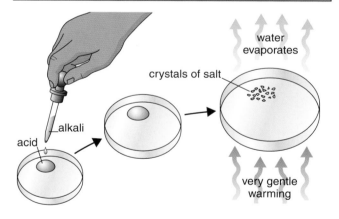

Figure 4   Place some drops of acid on a petri dish. Add the same amount of alkali. The water can be evaporated off leaving crystals of salt

The acidic hydrogen ions will combine with the alkaline hydroxide ions. They join together to make water particles. So two dangerous particles combine to make a neutral one. This is called **neutralisation**. The other parts of the acid and alkali solution are left behind when this happens. What is left forms a chemical called a salt.

Making salts

To make a salt you need an indicator to show up the change in pH of the solution. The acid and alkali are mixed together a little at a time until the solution is neutral. Then you will have the salt you want with no acid or alkali particles.

The coloured indicator can be removed using charcoal, and the water can be evaporated leaving the salt.

Naming the salt

First part of name from alkali	Second part of name from acid
sodium hydroxide makes '**sodium**'	hydrochloric acid makes '**chloride**'
potassium hydroxide makes '**potassium**'	sulphuric acid makes '**sulphate**'
calcium hydroxide makes '**calcium**'	nitric acid makes '**nitrate**'
magnesium hydroxide makes '**magnesium**'	ethanoic acid makes '**ethanoate**'

Table 2   Naming salts

Safety with acids

Oxidising
These substances provide oxygen which allows other materials to burn more fiercely.

Harmful
These substances are similar to toxic substances but less dangerous.

Highly flammable
These substances easily catch fire.

Corrosive
These substances attack and destroy living tissues, including eyes and skin.

Toxic
These substances can cause death. They may have their effects when swallowed or breathed in or absorbed through the skin.

Irritant
These substances are not corrosive but can cause reddening or blistering of the skin.

Figure 5   Common hazard symbols

Hazard labels are there to keep you safe. Make sure you know what they mean.

Concentrated acids

Figure 6   This is what concentrated acid does to cloth. Think what it could do to skin!

Concentrated acids are very dangerous. Only use very small quantities inside a fume cupboard.

Concentrated sulphuric acid is a heavy, oily liquid. When you mix it with water it transfers energy to its surroundings. This makes the liquids get very hot and boil.

The rule is to ADD ACID TO WATER.

NEVER add water to the concentrated acid.

Staying safe

1 **Protect your eyes at all times**
   It may not be your accident that causes you damage. Your eyes are by far the most easily damaged part of your body.

2 **Never lift chemicals above eye level**
   And don't crouch down near benches where there are chemicals.

3 **Treat contact with the skin or eyes with lots of cold water**
   Do it immediately, but don't run, as this could cause more accidents. Diluting chemicals helps to make them safe.

Hodder Science Summary Book

Safety equipment

Figure 7 Safety equipment in use in the laboratory

- Use safety glasses to prevent splashes of acid from getting into the eyes.
- Strong rubber gloves and rubber aprons are used by people who work a lot with strong acids.
- Eye-wash bottles of sterile water are kept wherever acids are being used.

IMPORTANT: Strong alkalis are just as dangerous as acids.

Revision

1 Write a school report for 'the best acid in the class'. Say how it is better than all other acids by explaining the different reactions that acids have.

   Include these scientific terms in your school report:

   **corrosive   alkali   salt   hazardous
   indicator   pH scale   neutralisation**

Questions

1 Bacteria on our teeth produce acid. What does the acid do to our teeth?

2 Soap is a very weak alkali. What does it feel like if you get it in your eyes?

3 What do you use to protect your eyes when working with hazardous chemicals?

4 Copy and complete this table opposite for Raman. He has done acidity tests on a range of solutions. Some have been tested with Universal Indicator paper and some with a pH meter.

5 Becca is going to do an experiment to neutralise hydrochloric acid with potassium hydroxide (an alkali). She has made some notes, but jotted them down in a random order. Sort out her notes and add to them, to write her a plan for her investigation.

   - Charcoal powder will absorb indicator particles.
   - Take care, wear goggles, wipe up spills.
   - Universal Indicator colour shows the pH.
   - Measure out the right amount of acid.
   - The mixture is neutral when the pH is 7.

Solution	Reading from pH meter	Colour of Universal Indicator paper
black coffee	15	
lime water	12	
blood	8	
sea water		green
milk		yellow
ammonia solution (surface cleaner)	11	
oven cleaner (sodium hydroxide)		purple
rust remover (phosphoric acid)		red

5.2 Chemical change

Key Words

corrosion	combustion
hydrogen	methane
carbonates	oxygen
carbon dioxide	equation
lime water	fire triangle
chemical change	fossil fuel

What munches metal?

Most metals react with acids. Hydrogen gas is produced from the acid. The metal gets dissolved and turned into a salt. Figure 1 shows the reaction between magnesium and hydrochloric acid and the equation below shows what the reaction makes.

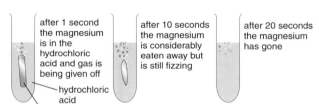

after 1 second the magnesium is in the hydrochloric acid and gas is being given off

hydrochloric acid

magnesium

after 10 seconds the magnesium is considerably eaten away but is still fizzing

after 20 seconds the magnesium has gone

Figure 1　The reaction between magnesium and hydrochloric acid

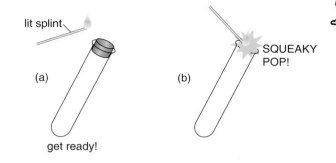

lit splint

(a)

get ready!

(b)

SQUEAKY POP!

Figure 2　a) Keep the gas in the test tube with a bung b) When you test the gas with a lighted splint, it will burn with a squeaky pop if it is hydrogen.

Figure 3　Baghi testing acids in the lab

magnesium + hydrochloric acid → magnesium chloride + hydrogen
(METAL)　　　　　(ACID)　　　　　　　(SALT)　　　　(GAS)

To see if hydrogen gas is made collect any created gases in a test tube and test as shown in Figure 2.

Baghi was sure all metals would dissolve in acid. He tried four metals and two acids. His results are shown in Table 1.

Test for hydrogen: use a lit splint and the gas explodes with a squeaky pop.

Metal	Hydrochloric acid	Sulphuric acid
zinc	fizzed steadily	fizzed steadily
copper	nothing happened	nothing happened
magnesium	fizzed very quickly and dissolved	fizzed very quickly and dissolved
iron	fizzed slowly	fizzed slowly

Table 1　Baghi's results

Figure 4 Camel urine is a liquid that is very corrosive to aeroplanes. If aeroplanes are carrying camels, their urine will eat through the metal floor!

Making a fizz

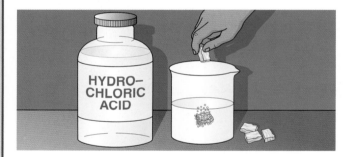

Figure 5 When the piece of marble is added to the hydrochloric acid it fizzes as carbon dioxide is released.

Marble is a beautiful stone but it gets attacked by acids. Acidic particles rip the calcium carbonate particles in the rock apart to make new substances. One of the new substances is carbon dioxide. Figure 6 shows how to test for carbon dixoide.

All carbonates will neutralise acids. The acidic particles rip the carbonates up, but are chemically changed when they do it. The bits left over make a salt.

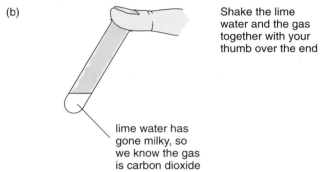

(a) chemical reaction

carbon dioxide

lime water

Carbon dioxide is heavier than air so it can be poured from one test tube to another

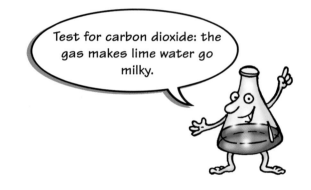

(b)

Shake the lime water and the gas together with your thumb over the end

lime water has gone milky, so we know the gas is carbon dioxide

Figure 6 Testing for carbon dioxide

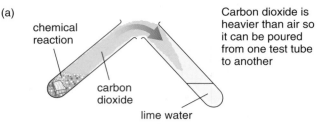

Test for carbon dioxide: the gas makes lime water go milky.

A nice change

Pancakes

Mandy can see different changes take place as she makes the pancakes.

- When she heats the fat it loses its shape and turns into a liquid.
- When she cooks the pancake mix, it turns from a liquid to a solid and keeps its shape.

calcium carbonate + hydrochloric acid → calcium chloride (SALT) + water + carbon dioxide (GAS)

Figure 7 In the café Mandy is making pancakes.

These are two different types of change.

When fat is heated it melts. When it cools again it solidifies. The solid fat is able to change into a liquid when it is hot and change back again when it cools. This is called a **physical change**.

When pancake mix is heated, the liquid turns into a solid shape. When it cools, it stays permanently in this shape. This is a **chemical change**.

The water cycle

This is a series of physical changes and is shown in Figure 8.

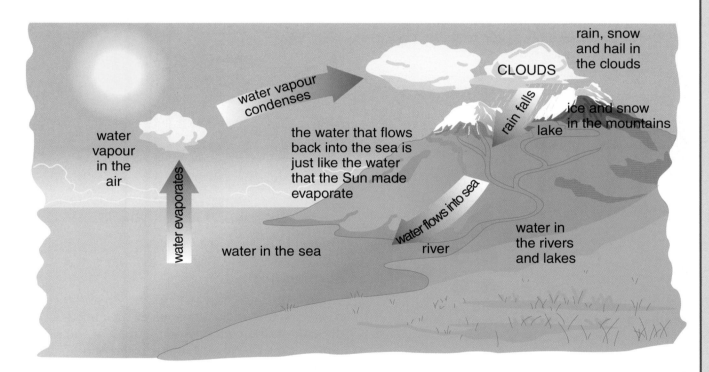

Figure 8 The water cycle

Fire

Fire has been our friend for over 400 000 years. Fire kept us warm and frightened away wild animals.

Fire is made when a fuel reacts with oxygen in the air. This is called an oxidation reaction. Oxygen combines with the fuel to make new substances. These are called oxides.

Fuels are made of molecules. The atoms that make up these molecules react with oxygen. The new molecules made in the chemical change contain less stored energy than the fuel molecules. This is because some energy is released. Normally it is released by heating but it could also be released as electricity or light.

The fuel we use as bottled gas is called propane. It is made of simple molecules containing three carbon atoms and eight hydrogen atoms. It needs five molecules of oxygen to 'burn' one molecule of propane.

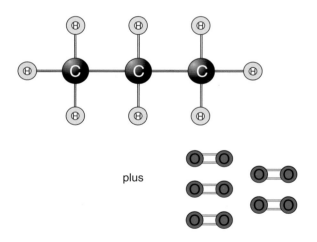

Figure 9   Propane reacts with oxygen . . .

When the propane and oxygen (Figure 9) have reacted (burned) the atoms change partners and make new molecules. They make carbon dioxide and water molecules (Figure 10).

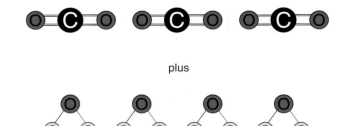

plus

Figure 10   . . . to produce carbon dioxide and water.

Exactly the same atoms are there. They have just swapped round to make bonds with new partners. Each of these bonds has an 'energy' value. The energy value of the bonds in carbon dioxide and water molecules adds up to less than the value of the bonds in propane and oxygen.

Figure 11   A propane gas burner

Burning hot

When fuels burn they use up oxygen and form new substances. The substances produced depend on the elements in the fuel. At the same time energy is released into the surroundings. For example, when natural gas is burned in air on a gas hob, the energy released is used to cook our food.

Fuels like coal, gas and oil are fossil fuels. They are found in rocks underground. They were made over millions of years from the remains of dead animals and plants.

Reactions like this, where energy is released from fuels, are called combustion reactions.

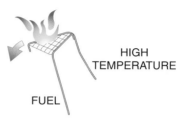

fossil fuel + oxygen → carbon dioxide + water + energy transfer

Fighting fire

Home fires kill about 500 people a year in the UK. Most of these fires begin accidentally, but how do they happen?

A fire needs three things to get it going:

- fuel
- oxygen
- a high temperature.

These are often shown as the fire triangle (Figure 14).

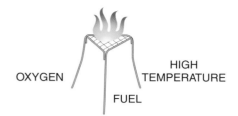

Figure 14 To keep a fire going steady you need all three things shown on the legs of the tripod.

Figure 12 A house on fire

Figure 15 To put a fire out you have to take away any one of the sides and the fire collapses. For example, to put out a chip pan fire, the fire fighter puts a fire blanket over it. This stops the supply of oxygen and the fire goes out.

Revision

1 Make **three** sets of cards to summarise information.

   a) Set 1: **fizz reactions.** This set of cards should contain facts about all the 'fizz' reactions of acids with metals and carbonates.

   b) Set 2: **testing for gases**. This set of cards has the detail of how to test to see if a gas is carbon dioxide or hydrogen.

   c) Set 3: **combustion**. This set of cards contains facts about fire and combustion reactions.

   Keep and use these cards as an aid to revision.

2 **Concept map**
   Combine all the sets of cards into a concept map on a big piece of paper. Show how there are links between the different chemical changes.

Figure 13 Forest fire in Indonesia, South-east Asia

Hodder Science Summary Book

Use the diagram below showing magnesium reacting with hydrochloric acid to answer questions 1–5.

1 What happens when the magnesium is first put in the acid?

2 What has happened to the solid magnesium metal at the end of the reaction?

3 Do all metals get changed by acids?

4 List all the things you would need to be able to test for hydrogen gas.

5 What is the name of the salt that is left when magnesium reacts with sulphuric acid?

6 What do you see when an acid reacts with pieces of marble?

7 What is the name of the gas given off?

8 How do you test a gas to see if it is carbon dioxide? Write a step-by-step method for doing the test.

Use the equation for burning propane gas below to answer questions 9–11.

$$C_3H8 + 5 O2 \rightarrow 3 CO2 + 4 H_2O$$

9 What is the formula for propane?

10 What is the formula of an oxygen molecule?

11 Write a word equation for the propane/oxygen reaction.

12 Copy the following table and use the idea of the fire triangle to complete it.

Method to stop fire	Why does the fire stop?
Pour water on a charcoal barbecue	
Cut down the trees in the path of a forest fire	
For a person whose clothes are on fire, wrap them in a blanket or large coat	

13 Explain what happens in the water cycle. Draw a quick diagram.

14 Name three fossil fuels.

15 Soot makes a Bunsen flame yellow sometimes, where does the soot come from?

16 Katie did some work investigating the amount of 'night light' candles that got burned away and how much they heated water. Here are her results.

Amount of candle burned (g)	0	3	5	8	10	14
Temperature of 100 g of water (°C)	20	36	46	62	72	92

a) Plot a graph of the results.

b) Put a line of best fit through the points.

c) What do you notice about the line?

d) How would you describe (in words) the relationship shown in the graph?

e) How much candle would be needed to boil the water?

5.3 Reactions of metals

Figure 1   Uses of the six most common metals (see text for details).

Key Words	
base	basic oxide
reactivity series	extraction
acidic oxide	alkali metals
alkaline oxide	

Metals and non-metals

Metals

There are about 70 metals but only a few are in common use.

Steel holds up most of our buildings, bridges and roadways. Iron in the form of steel is strong, hard and tough. Iron is 100% iron atoms. Steel is 99.6% iron atoms and 0.4% carbon atoms. Steel is much harder than iron. Copper, can be drawn out into wires. Shiny metals, such as silver and gold, can be bent into decorative shapes.

Figure 1 shows some uses of the six most common metals: a) Iron is used to make steel. b) Manganese is used in stainless steel. c) Copper is used for electrical wiring. d) Aluminium is used for airframes. e) Silver is used to make expensive ornaments. f) Gold stays shiny, so is used for jewellery.

	Metals	Non-metals
Surface texture	shiny	dull
Melting point	high temperatures	low temperatures
Hardness	hard	soft and easy to cut
Tensile strength	strong	weak
Brittleness	bend (flexible) can be drawn into wires (ductility) and hammered into flat sheets (malleability)	break very easily
Sound	ring like a bell when hit	make a dull thud when hit
Magnetism	iron (steel), nickel and cobalt are the only magnetic materials	no non-metals are magnetic
Conductivity	conduct electricity	do not conduct electricity (except carbon in the form of graphite)
Heat conductivity	metals allow energy to flow through them, causing heating	non-metals are poor at conducting energy to cause heating

Table 1   Comparing the common properties of metals and non-metals

Non-metals

There are only about 20 non-metal elements. Of these six are the unreactive noble gases. Organisms contain the non-metal elements carbon, oxygen, hydrogen and nitrogen. Silicon is the main element in most rocks. There are few non-metals, but they are some of the most important elements in our lives.

Acid patterns

Spectator ions

When acids dissolve in water, they split up to make hydrogen ions. These hydrogen ions are the 'acid reacting' particles. The other part of an acid is a 'spectator ion'.

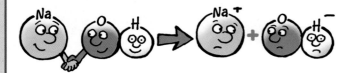

HCl splits into H^+ (hydrogen ions) and Cl^- (chloride ions).

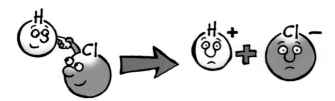

HNO_3 splits into H^+ (hydrogen ions) and $NO3^-$ (nitrate ions).

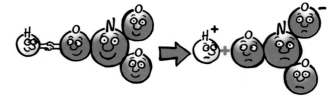

When an alkali dissolves, it also splits into different particles. The hydroxide ion is the 'alkali reacting' particle. The other part of an alkali is a 'spectator ion'.

NaOH splits into Na^+ (sodium ions) and OH^- (hydroxide ions).

When acids and alkalis react in a neutralisation reaction, the spectator ions take no part. They stay dissolved in the solution.

Neutralisation: example A

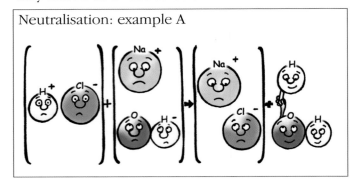

Neutralisation: example B

If you remove the spectator ions, both neutralisation equations are exactly the same:

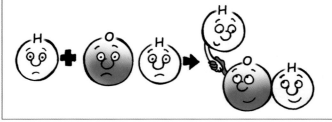

Making salts

When acids get neutralised and water molecules get left, the 'spectator ions' are left as a solution. These make a salt. There are lots of different salts – some of them have common names as well as chemical names.

Acid treatment

A chemical base will neutralise an acid and make water molecules in the reaction.

Don't confuse the chemical word 'base' with all the other meanings of the word base. Alkalis are a particular sort of chemical base. They are metal oxides that dissolve in water to form a 'hydroxide' solution.

Also reactive metals combine with acids by displacing hydrogen from the acid compound, but no water molecules are produced.

Here are some important acid reactions and some examples.

> All acids react with substances in the same ways.

1 Acid plus metal oxide

$$(H^+ \text{ and } H^+ \text{ and } SO_4^{2-}) + MgO \rightarrow (Mg^{2+} \text{ and } SO_4^{2-}) + H_2O$$
sulphuric acid   magnesium   magnesium   water
oxide   sulphate

2 Acid plus carbonate

$$(H^+ \text{ and } H^+ \text{ and } SO_4^{2-}) + MgCO_3 \rightarrow (Mg^{2+} \text{ and } SO_4^{2-}) + H_2O + CO_2$$
sulphuric acid   magnesium   magnesium   water   carbon
carbonate   sulphate   dioxide

3 Acid plus metal – a less predictable reaction

$$(H^+ \text{ and } H^+ \text{ and } SO_4^{2-}) + Mg \rightarrow (Mg^{2+} \text{ and } SO_4^{2-}) + H_2$$
sulphuric acid   magnesium   magnesium   hydrogen
sulphate   gas

The third reaction is like a displacement reaction. The magnesium metal takes the place of the hydrogen in the sulphuric acid and steals the sulphate ion away from the hydrogen

Figure 2 Rust remover. Phosphoric acid is used to dissolve rust off iron and steel. The iron oxide is dissolved quickly by the acid but the acid is weak and only dissolves the iron metal slowly.

Figure 3 Kettle scale (top). Acids are also used to dissolve the limescale that gets on kettle elements (bottom). Limescale is calcium carbonate (like chalk).

Metal and non-metal oxides

Rainbow chemicals

Figure 4   Solution of the oxides of (from left to right) sodium, calcium, aluminium, silicon, phosphorus, sulphur and chlorine. These elements are in the third row of the Periodic Table.

If an indicator is put in the solution a rainbow of colour results. Aluminium oxide and silicon oxide are not soluble, so the yellowy-green colour of jars three and four is the colour Universal Indicator goes with water.

The metal oxides all neutralise acids. Substances that neutralise acids are called bases. Aluminium oxide is insoluble, but neutralises acids so it is a base. Sodium oxide and calcium oxide are bases and they dissolve to form alkaline solutions.

Phosphorus oxide and sulphur dioxide dissolve to produce strongly acidic solutions. Chlorine oxide is also acid. Silicon dioxide will react like an acidic oxide but is insoluble. So non-metal oxides act like acids.

> Non-metal oxides make acids.
> Metal oxides neutralise acids.
> They are called bases.

Testing a gas: oxygen

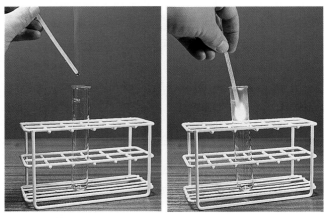

Figure 5   Set light to a wooden splint. Blow it out so it is just glowing. Put it in oxygen gas and it burns so well that it bursts into flame again.

Metals

Over millions of years, all the metals on Earth except gold reacted with oxygen. They became metal oxides and were part of the rocks. The metal oxides are no use to us, but the metals are very useful. Gold was rare and precious.

Ten thousand years ago every home, big or small, cave or palace had a fire. Humans built fires on rocks to keep them under control. When the fires were cleaned out, shiny blobs of copper metal were found and necklaces were made out of them.

Seven thousand years ago the Afghan people were deliberately 'smelting' rocks with charcoal to get copper. The carbon in the charcoal changed the copper oxide to copper. The carbon is more reactive than the copper. It will steal the oxygen away from it. Copper oxide and carbon became carbon dioxide and copper.

Five thousand years ago people found out about bronze. Mixing rocks containing copper and tin made a metal that was much harder than either copper or tin on their own.

Three thousand years ago people living near the Black Sea in eastern Europe could make iron. Making iron needs high temperatures. Carbon is used to reduce iron oxide to iron. People used the iron to make tools and weapons. Iron was very much harder than bronze.

The Romans came to Britain 2000 years ago. They used the copper and tin mines here. They also made lead metal. Lead pipes have been found in Roman remains.

The more reactive metals can only be produced by ripping compounds apart with electricity. Aluminium was a precious metal in the time of Napoleon in the early 1800s.

Now we know about 70 or more metals. Most were discovered in the last 150 years.

Some metals react much more easily and more vigorously than others. There is a league table for the reactivity of metals called the reactivity series.

The reactivity series

magnesium – most reactive

aluminium

zinc

iron

lead

copper

silver

gold – less reactive

Metals that are higher in the reactivity series will displace metals that are lower than them from their compounds. Displacement reactions are often used to find out where an element is in the reactivity series.

Figure 6 Metals react differently with the oxygen in the air when heated. Copper (a) goes black but magnesium (b) bursts into flame.

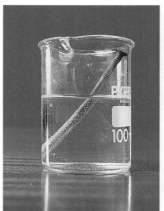

Figure 7 Metals react at different rates with acids. Iron (a) fizzes very slowly, but magnesium (b) dissolves very quickly. They both displace hydrogen from the acid.

Figure 8 Zinc has displaced copper from copper sulphate solution.

Reactivity to order

Alkali metals are the most reactive of all the metals. They occupy the top places in the reactivity series.

Alkali metals are caustic – they will attack and damage flesh. They make slimy soap out of your flesh and they do it very quickly. The damage they cause is painful and particularly dangerous to the eyes.

Sodium hydroxide's common name is caustic soda. It is used for cleaning ovens and unblocking drains. It turns the muck blocking the drain into soapy slime that can be washed away.

Metals have battles with each other. The more reactive metal wins.

The alkali metals

This is a really spectacular set of elements. They are the most reactive of all the metals. They react rapidly with oxygen in the air – so rapidly that they must be stored in oil.

Figure 9 Lithium reacts rapidly with water, producing hydrogen gas. The lithium dissolves and becomes lithium hydroxide solution.

Figure 10 Sodium gets melted by the heat released as it reacts with water. The molten blob races round the surface on a cushion of hydrogen gas.

Figure 11 Potassium reacts so rapidly that it bursts into flame when it is in contact with water. The material burning is the hydrogen gas produced by the reaction. The lilac colour is caused by potassium particles getting heated in the flame.

Figure 12 Rubidium reacts so rapidly that the heat from the burning hydrogen makes the metal explode and fly about the room. Rubidium is very caustic, so this is far too dangerous to do in a school laboratory. People would be blinded!

Figure 13 WOW!! The reaction between caesium and water is even more explosive.

Revision

1 Make a quiz about the properties of metals. The answers to the questions must form a list of words that goes from A–Z. Work with a partner, swap quizzes with another pair and work out their answers.

2 Make a card for each metal. Include the colour and uses of the metal on the card. Ensure you mention where the metal is in the reactivity series for metals and how it reacts with oxygen and acids.

Keep the cards in reactivity series order.

Hodder Science Summary Book

1 When most metals are heated in air, what new materials do they become?

2 These 'new materials' are heavier than the original metals. Where has the extra mass come from?

3 What are the properties of metals? (*Hint*: there are nine properties.)

4 Explain what alloys are.

5 Pure iron can be strengthened. How is this commonly done and what name do we give the resulting material?

6 Draw particle pictures for sulphuric acid (H_2SO_4) being neutralised by calcium hydroxide solution ($Ca(OH)_2$).

7 Copy and complete the table below about neutralisation and salts.

8 What is the difference between alkalis and bases in chemistry?

9 Cola, the drink, contains some phosphoric acid. What would you see if a piece of rusty iron was put in cola overnight?

10 Why do we use weak acids to get rid of limescale in coffee machines?

11 What is the fizzy gas given off when acids are used to remove limescale?

12 Explain how you know that a chemical reaction is happening between copper oxide and zinc metal?

13 a) What element is used to remove the oxygen from iron ore in a blast furnace?

   b) What produces the heat in a blast furnace?

   c) Write a word equation for the production of iron.

14 Deepak works as a structural engineer. He uses a huge machine that tests steel bars until they break. Many steel bridges are getting rusty, so Deepak is testing the strength of samples of old steel. He makes his test fair by cutting the same size samples. The table shows his results.

   a) Average the results of the tests.

   b) Draw a chart to display the results.

   c) How reliable are the test results for steel after
   i) 10 years
   ii) 150 years?

   d) Write a short report, based on the results, about replacing the bridges.

   e) Until the 150 year old bridge gets replaced, what is the maximum safe load that the steel can take?

Name of acid	Name of alkali	Name of salt
nitric acid	potassium hydroxide	
sulphuric acid	magnesium hydroxide	
		potassium sulphate
		lithium chloride
phosphoric acid	calcium hydroxide	

| Age of bridge | Breaking strength (tonnes) | | |
	1st test	2nd test	3rd test
New	12	12	11
10 years old	12	11	11
20 years old	10	11	11
30 years old	11	12	11
50 years old	8	9	10
100 years old	7	7	8
150 years old	1	4	5

5.4 Using chemistry

Key Words

temperature	exothermic
energy transfer	plastic
chemical bonds	monomer
endothermic	polymer

The rules of the game

1 Energy and temperature

All matter is made of particles. These particles can be atoms, molecules or ions. The particles in matter are moving all the time. As matter gets hotter, the particles have more energy, so they move faster and faster. The motion of particles makes smells spread.

Figure 2   Do you remember the carnival model of states of matter?

3 Energy transfers

Energy is *taken in* when chemical bonds are broken apart. Energy is *released* when chemical bonds are remade.

When fuels burn, more energy is released than is taken in. The extra energy heats up the surroundings.

4 How chemical reactions work

- Metal with non-metal: metal atoms have few outer electrons. When they form compounds, they get rid of these electrons. The outer shells of non-metals are nearly full. They accept the electrons from the metals

Figure 3   A metal reacting with a non-metal

Figure 1   Francis often had smelly cheese for lunch, which made him very unpopular.

2 States of matter

In solids, particles are neatly arranged and are vibrating. You can only get at the outermost particles.

In liquids, the particles are a milling, mixing, close-packed crowd.

In gases, the particles are all flying about separately past each other, and are easy to get at.

- Non-metal with non-metal. All non-metal atoms have outer shells that are nearly full. They will share electrons with each other to get enough electrons to have a full shell. The electrons have to orbit both atoms, so this holds the atoms together in a little group. This is a molecule.

5 Conservation of mass

Matter cannot be created or destroyed in chemical reactions.

Figure 4   What has happened here?

Charcoal burns away on a barbecue, so that only a scrap of ash is left. But the atoms of carbon that make up the charcoal have not ceased to exist – they have become carbon dioxide in the air. When the tree next to the barbecue grows bigger, it is not creating atoms out of nothing. It uses the carbon from the carbon dioxide in the air. Of course this takes years, not minutes.

Poison gas, combustion and explosions

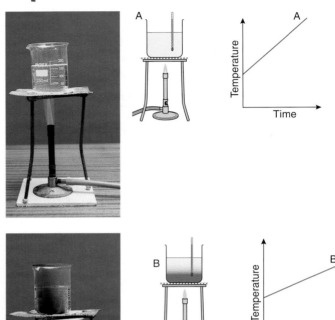

Figure 5   Burner A has a clean blue flame. Burner B has a yellow flame made by glowing soot particles. The beaker has become all sooty.

Burner A is transferring more energy per second than burner B. This is because burner A has the correct air/methane mixture.

Burner B has too little air to completely burn the gas, so less energy is transferred. Some is left in the unburned soot particles.

Equation A

$$CH_4 + 2O_2 \rightarrow CO_2 + 2H_2O$$
methane   oxygen   carbon dioxide   water

Equation B

$$CH_4 + O_2 \rightarrow C + 2H_2O$$
methane   oxygen   soot   water

Hydrogen is easier to oxidise than carbon, so the water gets formed first in the combustion reaction.

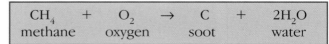

Matches

A match is like a mini controlled firework. Its head contains:

- carbon, to burn rapidly

- sulphur, to burn rapidly

- potassium chlorate, to provide the oxygen.

The equation for the reaction is:

$$KCIO_4 + S + C \rightarrow KCL + SO_2 + CO_2$$

potassium chlorate   sulphur   carbon   potassium chloride   sulphur dioxide   carbon dioxide

All the oxygen for the reaction is in the compounds of the match head. The sulphur dioxide is the choking, acidic gas you can smell when a match has been struck.

Hot food and cold relief

All changes – chemical and physical – involve energy transfers, otherwise they would not happen.

Figure 6   This coffee gets heated by a chemical reaction in part of the can

Making cold

Chemical changes can produce cold. To do this they take in energy. As the particles are separated, energy is taken in. Most cooking reactions are endothermic – they need heat to keep them going.

100 g of water + 10 g sodium thiosulphate crystals

Before mixing	After dissolving
20°C	6°C

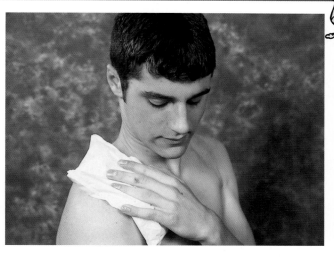

Figure 7   Twist the pack and it gets cold enough to numb the pain of a sporting injury. Injuries such as sprains or bruises hurt because of the swelling. Cold helps to reduce the swelling. The chemicals combine to take in energy, so the pack gets cold. This is called an endothermic reaction.

Making heating

Many chemical changes cause heating. For example, acid particles combine with alkali particles to make water molecules. This is putting particles together, so it gives out energy as heat.

25 cm³ of acid solution + 25 cm³ of alkali solution

Before mixing	After mixing
20°C	29°C

Electricity from metals

Metals burn in oxygen and cause heating. Metals dissolve in acids and cause heating.

If the metal is in an electric cell and the cell is connected in a circuit, then the chemical energy stored in the metal can be transferred as electricity. Metals that are high up the reactivity series release more energy than those which are lower down in the series. The voltage of the cell measures how much energy the electrons are carrying.

Figure 8 This electric cell is made from the reactive metal and the non-reactive carbon (graphite) rod in a conducting solution (salt water).

In control

We control chemical reactions to make less useful chemicals into more useful ones.

We control chemical reactions so that we can transfer the maximum amount of energy from chemical changes.

We control chemical reactions so that we can clean up dirt, waste and pollution, and stop them from harming the environment.

Manufactured materials
Polymers

Plastics are all manufactured materials called polymers. Manufactured polymers were invented in the last century, but many natural materials are polymers. Proteins, starch, cellulose and DNA are all polymers. Polymers are made up of smaller molecules, called monomers, all joined together.

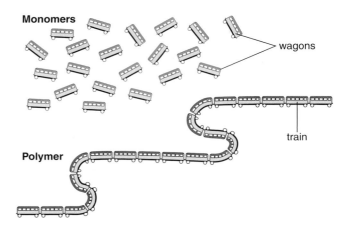

Figure 10 A good model for monomers joining together to make polymers is the wagons of a train. One difference is that thousands of monomer molecules get joined together to make polymer molecules. This would be several kilometres long if it were a train.

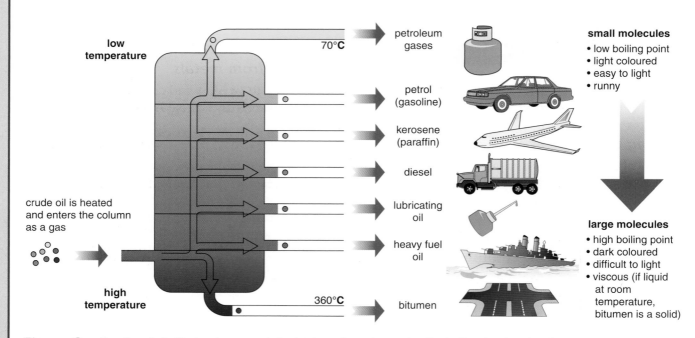

Figure 9 Fractional distillation 'sorts out' the hydrocarbons in crude oil. Similar-sized molecules come out at the same level

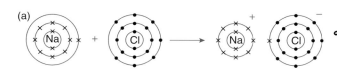

Crude oil (petroleum) is a liquid mixture of lots of different hydrocarbons (which are polymers). Because they have different boiling points, they can be separated by fractional distillation. In the natural mixture we call crude oil, there are as many 'fuel oil' molecules as 'petrol' molecules, but there is much more demand for petrol (for cars) than for fuel oil (for oil-fired central heating) – even in the winter.

Ideal partners

Alkali metals are very reactive metals. The halogens are reactive non-metals. They form very stable compounds together. The best known is common salt – sodium chloride. Common salt has a multitude of uses as well as going on chips.

The alkali metals of Group 1 start every new row of the Periodic Table. All the alkali metals have just one electron in their new outermost shell.

The halogens of Group 7 are at the end of the row, just before the noble gases. The halogens have one electron missing from their outer shell.

This explains the similarity between the two groups as 'families' of elements.

An alkali metal atom loses one electron when it reacts to form a positive ion.

A halogen atom gains one electron when it reacts to form a negative ion.

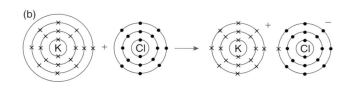

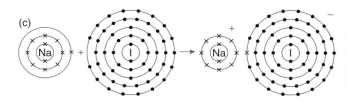

Figure 12 Sodium and potassium atoms react in the way described above. It is very easy to lose just one electron in this way. That is why the alkali metals are so reactive. It is also very easy to pick up one extra electron. That is why the halogens are so reactive.

Revision

1 Chapters 4 and 5 of this book provide a summary of how the chemistry part of science works. This includes kinetic theory, what substances there are and how different particles can be combined to make useful substances. Make brief notes about each section of the two chapters (no more than one side of A4 per section). Include diagrams and sketches. Then take a pen and highlight the most important points in your pages of notes.

Keep these as a revision aid.

Questions

1 Write a few sentences to explain the idea of 'movement and temperature' to a junior school pupil. Use only words that a nine-year-old would understand.

2 Why does burning hydrogen gas in oxygen transfer energy and cause heating?

Figure 11 Salt makes ice melt at a lower temperature. When it's icy, the council puts salt on roads to keep them free of ice.

Questions

3 Look at the table of observations about iron nails below. Galvanising means coating the iron with zinc (zinc metal is more reactive than iron).

   a) What two substances together cause rust?

   b) Why does paint protect against rust?

   c) Why is galvanising not like painting?

4 a) What are polymers?

   b) What is a monomer?

   c) How do you get polymers with different properties?

5 Magnesium burns in air in the following reaction:

magnesium + oxygen → magnesium oxide

$$Mg \quad + \quad O_2 \quad \rightarrow \quad MgO$$

Balance the symbol equation.

6 Copper carbonate dissolves in sulphuric acid, producing lots of froth and fizz by the following reaction:

$$CuCO_3 + H_2SO_4 \rightarrow CuSO_4 + H_2O + CO_2$$

Write the word equation for the reaction.

7 Concrete needs carbon dioxide to set properly.

   calcium + carbon → calcium
   oxide   dioxide   carbonate

Write the symbol equation for the reaction.

8 Ethanol burns to release heat energy.

ethanol + oxygen → carbon dioxide + water

$$C_2H_5OH \quad + \quad O_2 \quad \rightarrow \quad CO_2 \quad + \quad H_2O$$

Copy and balance the symbol equation.

9 Sulphuric acid will react with sodium hydroxide that has been used to strip paint off doors.

$$H_2SO_4 + NaOH \rightarrow Na_2SO_4 + H_2O$$

Copy and balance the symbol equation and write the word equation

10 Match these types of reaction to those detailed in questions 5–9.

- **acid/base** - **neutralisation**
- **combustion** - **oxidation**
- **metal oxide/non-metal oxide**

11 Serena is an environmental techician. She is investigating how fast acid rain will attack marble statues. She is given some data that she plots to make the series of graphs shown in the diagram.

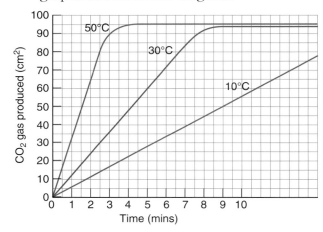

   a) What is the maximum amount of gas produced in the experiment?

   b) Why do the first two graphs level off?

   c) Why doesn't the 10°C graph level off?

   d) What could Serena say about the speed at which marble gets attacked by acid?

   e) Design a method for protecting the statues from attack by acid rain. Draw a picture or diagram of how this would work.

Table 1 Question 3

Nail in air	Nail in boiled water (no dissolved oxygen)	Nail in water (with dissolved oxygen)	Painted nail in water	Galvanised nail in water
no rust	no rust	goes rusty	no rust – but rusty where paint flakes off	no rust – even where coating is damaged

Rocks and the environment

6.1 Driving the rock cycle

Key Words

igneous	magma
metamorphic	continental drift
sedimentary	tectonic plate
crust	earthquake
mantle	volcano
lava	

Solids and liquids in the Earth

Making rocks

The Earth is 4600 million years old. Over millions of years there have been big changes.

Mountain ranges rise up as one continent pushes against another. Sun, rain, freezing cold and wind break up the mountains into smaller rocks. Water in rivers carries away and wears the rocks until they are sand or silt.

Below the **crust** is the **mantle (1)**. The mantle contains very hot rock under very high pressure. Normally at such high temperatures the rock would be liquid but the high pressure keeps it like a plastic.

Igneous rock (2 and 3)

Rock from the mantle can be squeezed into the crust. It turns into a very hot liquid, called **magma**. This makes **igneous rock**. As the rock is pushed into the crust it cools. If it cools slowly, large crystals can form. If it cools a lot faster the crystals are a lot smaller. If the magma breaks through the crust it produces volcanoes and the liquid rock is called **lava**.

Rocks get worn away but it takes millions of years.

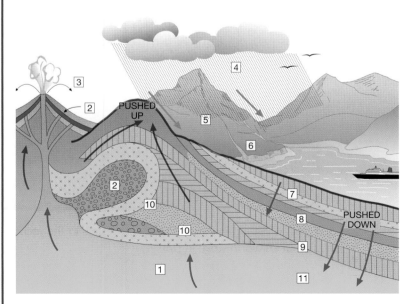

Figure 1   The rock cycle

Sedimentary rock (4 to 8)

Sand and mud get washed to the sea. Over millions of years the layers of sand get thicker and thicker. The layers deep down are squeezed so much that they turn into rock. This is called **sedimentary rock**. This rock is made of small grains cemented together by chemical salts.

Heat and pressure (9 and 10)

As millions of years go by the layers of sedimentary rock get buried deeper and deeper.

Metamorphic rock is made when buried sedimentary and igneous rock gets heated and compressed. The old rock turns into new material. The new material can be similar in colour to the old rock, but there are differences in texture and it is baked much harder. The rocks are compressed because of the pressure from the layers of rocks above the metamorphic rock. The heating comes from the mantle below.

An example is marble, it is a beautiful smooth stone but it was once grainy limestone.

Mantle again (11)

The rocks get pushed down and down. They are heated, melted, then put under pressure until they become part of the plastic mantle again. The rock cycle has gone around once.

Making new rocks

70% of all rocks on the Earth's surface are sedimentary. Making new rock is a very wet process.

Small fragments of sand and rock settle out from slow moving water and layers of sediment build up. There are distinct layers in the rock that is formed.

As the layers are compressed, they dry out. The salts and minerals from the water 'glue' the particles together into solid rock.

Limestone is a type of sedimentary rock, but not all limestone looks the same. It all depends what other materials got washed down the same river when the limestone formed.

Limestone is mainly calcium carbonate, but other materials change its colour and texture.

Sedimentary rocks get formed in layers. They are made on a sea bed.

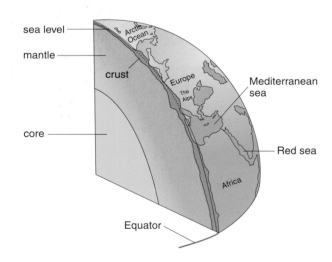

Figure 2 The Earth is not solid. It is like a ball of porridge with a thin crust.

Figure 3 The layers or strata are visible in the rock here at Lulworth Cove in Dorset.

The rocks at Lulworth Cove were folded by the same geological event that pushed up the Alps to form Europe's main mountain range. The result is this magnificent display of strata, now exposed to our view by weathering (Figure 3).

Fossils

Figure 4   These tropical ferns were found in rocks in Germany. It shows that the climate must have changed dramatically.

Fossils are formed in the following way:

1 The animal or plant dies and its remains fall into the sediment.

2 Soft parts decay, leaving just the harder material.

3 Sediments form their layers round the harder material.

4 Over a long period of time, the plant or animal remains are replaced by deposits of minerals in the rock.

5 The mineral deposits exactly match the shape of the plant and animal remains.

6 The sedimentary layers are exposed at the surface.

The fossil record is used to discover what life was like long ago.

Plate movements

The rock surface of the Earth is at most 10 kilometres thick and this planet is nearly 1200 kilometres in diameter. Beneath the rocky surface is a hot liquid rock called magma.

The crust is not in one piece. It is formed of huge plates (Figure 5 page 102). The movements in the magma under the crust drag the plates around the surface of the Earth. This movement of the plates is called plate tectonics.

Many years ago it was noticed that some parts of the world seemed to fit together although they were now many thousands of miles apart. If you look at a map of the world you will see that the eastern coastline of South America seems to fit into the western coastline of Africa. This is not a coincidence, they were once one landmass called Gondwanaland. Then they split apart, slowly moving to their present positions.

Solid rock

Pure substances melt and boil at fixed temperatures. Adding impurities changes the melting and boiling point of a substance.

Particles in solids

Each particle in a solid has a fixed place. But these particles are not standing still. All of the particles are vibrating all the time.

Substances melt when the rapid vibrations of their particles have enough energy to break the forces holding them together. These vibrations get quicker as the temperature gets hotter.

When liquid materials cool down the particles move slower and slower until they link together in regular patterns. When a large amount of a molten substance is cooling, the solid state forms in many places throughout it. If it is cooling slowly, the solid 'pieces' form slowly and are widely spaced. If it is cooling quickly, lots of much smaller solid 'pieces' form as they start much closer together.

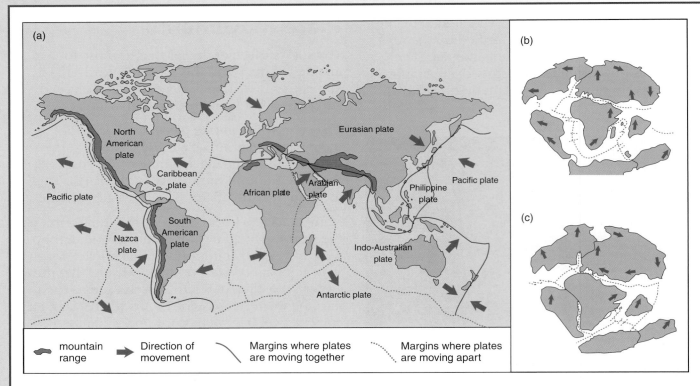

Figure 5 The surface of the Earth is made of plates that are slowly moving about. The movements cause volcanoes and earthquakes. (a) Distribution of the plates today. (b) The continents as they were 70 million years ago. (c) The continents 140 million years ago

Each solid 'piece' that forms from the liquid is a **crystal**. The process is called **crystallisation**.

This effect is seen very clearly in rocks that have been formed from molten magma or lava such as granite and basalt (Figure 6).

The melting point is linked to the hardness of the substance. Both melting point and hardness depend on the forces between the particles in the solid.

Figure 6 Granite rock is formed deep under the surface. Magma cools slowly to produce large crystals.

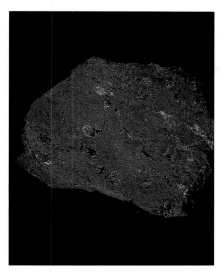

Figure 7   Basalt is a volcanic rock. The lava flows and cools very rapidly. This makes small, tightly-packed crystals.

Brave new island

Figure 8   An aerial view of Surtsey

As the Earth's surface moves, some molten magma gets to the surface. This effect produces volcanoes. They make new igneous rocks. In November 1963, a fresh volcano broke through the waves off Iceland, creating the world's youngest island, Surtsey. Columns of ash were sent almost 10 000 m into the air. Eruption followed eruption until the core of Surtsey, made of solidified rock, was holding its own against the waves. The new island now rises more than 170 metres above sea level.

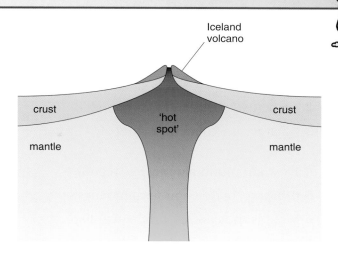

Figure 9   The formation of a volcano

Iceland is part of a chain of underwater mountains that runs down the centre of the Atlantic Ocean and marks the place where the North American plate is pulling apart from the European and African plates.

The volcanoes are caused by 'sea floor spreading'.

Another volcanic island is Hawaii. The piles of lava that form Hawaii rise as high as 9750 metres from the ocean floor. They have been built up to form the cone-shaped island.

Revision

1   This section contains two big ideas – the rock cycle and how tectonic plate movements cause **earthquakes** and **volcanoes.**

Make a flow chart for each of these.

Create a **rock cycle** flow chart. Include links between these terms:

**lava   igneous   crystallisation
magma   metamorphic   weathering
erosion   sedimentary   cementation
strata.**

2   Create a volcano flow chart. Draw diagrams of each stage of a volcano as it grows bigger. Include labels about where the material comes from.

3   Create an earthquake flow chart. Draw a flow chart to explain how the Earth's crust gets more and more stressed and then finally causes an earthquake.

Hodder Science Summary Book

Questions

1 What is the difference between a rock and a mineral?

2 Name two rocks and two minerals.

3 What are the materials you have chosen used for?

4 How are mountain ranges created?

5 What wears down mountain ranges?

6 What is the centre of the Earth like?

7 How is igneous rock made?

8 What are the rocks made from layers of sand and mud called?

9 What is metamorphic rock?

10 What sort of rock gets turned into metamorphic rock?

11 Deep down in the Earth, molten rock can gather in chambers that feed volcanoes. What is this molten rock called?

13 What are strata?

14 How do the sedimentary rock particles get stuck together?

15 Draw a cartoon strip (four pictures with captions) of layers of sedimentary particles settling out in the sea, getting buried by more layers, then drying out and finally becoming sedimentary rock.

16 While she was making candles, Sahera investigated the melting point of stearic acid and paraffin wax. Her results are shown in the table below.

a) Plot graphs for Sahera's investigation. These graphs are called cooling curves.

b) Explain why she decided that paraffin wax was a mixture and stearic acid was not.

c) What was the melting point of stearic acid?

Time (mins)	Cooling stearic acid /°C	Cooling paraffin wax /°C
0	90	90
1	84	83
2	79	77
3	75	72
4	69	66
5	69	61
6	69	60
7	69	59
8	69	58
9	65	57
10	63	56
11	60	52
12	58	49

Table 1   Sahera's results

6.2 Weathering and erosion

Key Words

erosion
physical weathering
chemical weathering
freeze/thaw cycle
scree slope
onion skin process
mineral

rock
hard water
acid rain
stalactite
stalagmite
fossil

The scrubbed face of the UK

These mountains in Scotland used to be part of North America. The process of continental drift carried the rocks here. The peaks are granite left over by erosion of the softer rock.

Wind and rain wear down the rocks. Rivers carry bits away.

Under this bleak moorland, the rock is full of caves and caverns.

Rainwater is a very weak acid, it chemically dissolves the rock away. Eventually, under the ground, huge spaces are left in the rock.

Edinburgh Castle is built on a lump of very hard volcanic rock left behind when the softer rock surrounding it was eroded away.

The surface of the Earth is constantly being changed. The solid surface of the Earth is constantly being scoured away. Physical processes split the rocks up then wind and water carry the bits away.

Rock movements can be slow, steady pushes that take millions of years. These fold the rock layers into new shapes.

Rocks and minerals

Rocks are made from grains of minerals.

A mineral is a pure crystalline substance that is found in the Earth's crust. Rocks are a mixture of lots of bits of minerals together.

A mineral is often just one colour. Rocks are not just one colour, they often look speckled. The process of erosion has mixed the minerals to make rock.

Minerals	Rocks
quartz	sandstone
olivine	limestone
iron pyrites	slate
malachite	granite
calcite	marble

Table 2   Some common minerals and rocks

There are three classes of rock types:

- **igneous rocks** – formed from molten material from inside the Earth

- **sedimentary rocks** – formed when water deposits layers of material

- **metamorphic rocks** – formed by the action of heating and pressure on other rocks.

A million year mixer

Weather and water break up rock. The process of weathering and the water and wind carrying the particles away is called 'erosion'.

Mechanical weathering

- When water freezes in cracks in the rock it expands and splits the rock.

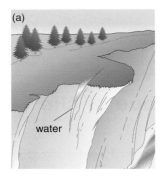
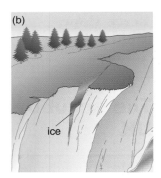

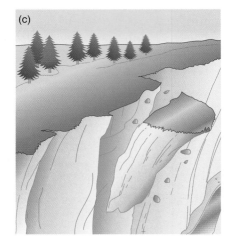

Figure 1   a) Water can fill cracks in the rock. If it is cold, the water will freeze. b) Water expands when it freezes. c) When this is repeated several times, it splits the rock.

Freezing water and hot sun can crack solid rock.

- Repeated heating and cooling can cause rocks to split. This is known as 'onion skin' weathering.

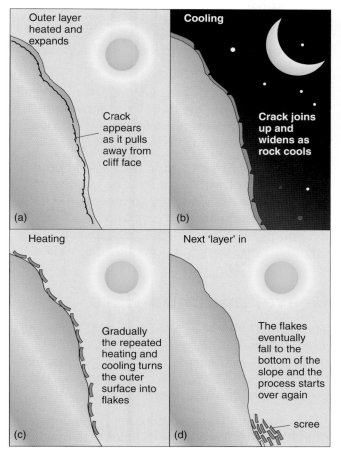

Figure 2 In the hot sun, one side of a rock can heat and expand while the other stays cool. The expansion can cause the rock to split.

- Seeds can grow in the cracks of rocks. The roots force themselves into the cracks, making them bigger. This is another form of mechanical weathering.

- Strong winds blow sand over the rocks and wear away softer rock from below harder rock leaving hard rock outcrops.

- The constant beating of the waves eventually breaks off parts of the cliffs.

- Huge heavy sheets of ice called glaciers break up rock and carry it away.

Chemical weathering

Figure 3 Limestone caves in Barbados

Chemical weathering turns rock into new materials by chemical action.

Rainwater is slightly acidic. Carbon dioxide from the atmosphere dissolves in rainwater to make a weak acid called **carbonic acid**. Limestone is a very alkaline rock so it is attacked by any acid. Limestone is a rock that contains a lot of calcium carbonate.

> Calcium carbonate + carbonic acid → calcium hydrogen carbonate
> $$CaCO_3 + H_2CO_3 \rightarrow Ca(HCO_3)_2$$
> (solid) (rain water) (solution)

Calcium compounds in rock can get dissolved in water. So these calcium compounds can get into the water supply to houses. This is called **hard water**.

Hard water is very healthy to drink as we need calcium and the other minerals in our bodies. But it can cause 'limescale' which is found in kettles and other water heaters.

Acid rain pollution

Sulphuric acid and nitric acid are made when gases such as sulphur dioxide and nitrogen oxide dissolve in rain clouds. This adds greatly to the slight natural acidity of rainwater.

'Acid rain' has become a severe problem over the last 100 years. It severely damages buildings and monuments, particularly those made out of limestone or marble.

Figure 4 One of these monuments is in London and has been damaged by acid rain.

Grand Canyon story

Figure 5 The Grand Canyon in Arizona, USA

How was the Grand Canyon formed?

The soil in the Grand Canyon is baked by the Sun and cannot absorb water when the rains come. Water comes down in torrents and the soil is quickly washed away.

These torrents can move boulders the size of small houses.

Before the building of the Glen Canyon dam, all the water from the melting of the snow in the Colorado Rockies came pouring down through the Grand Canyon in late Spring.

The Colorado River's spring floods scoured the bed of the river with all of this fast moving material. This has slowly eaten away at the banks and bed of the river. As a result it cut down deeper into the lower rock layers, making the one mile deep trench it flows through today.

Gravel and mud flats

The River Thames has a shallow, wide valley. All along the river valley material has been transported by the running water. This material has been sorted by size, according to how fast the river was flowing.

Upstream from London there are huge deposits of gravel – small stones with diameters ranging from 5 millimetres to a few centimetres. Gravel is a useful building material so is dug out. Thorpe Park, an amusement park in Surrey, near London, is built on a gravel pit.

Smaller sandy particles settled out in what is now the London area so the ground there is very sandy. Tiny particles got carried furthest. They have made the mud flats of the Thames Estuary.

Weathering mixes up the minerals in rock, then flowing water carries them away and sorts them out by size.

Fast-running water carries fragments of rock. These settle out when the water slows down.

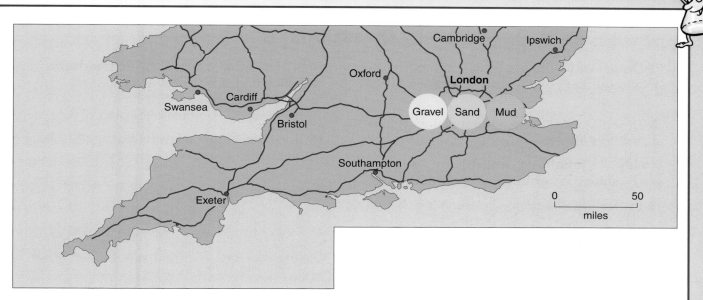

Figure 6 The London Basin

Revision

1 Take a large piece of paper and draw annotated diagrams of these processes:

- **acid rain weathering**
- **freeze/thaw weathering**
- **forming a scree slope**
- **onion skin weathering**
- **making sedimentary rock layers.**

Colour the diagrams and add clear labels describing the processes. Put them up on the wall near where you revise.

Remember the surface of the earth gets worn down, washed away and made into new rock in a continuous cycle.

Hodder Science Summary Book

1 Design and write out a fair test method to find out how much water a pebble will soak up.

2 Describe what these natural materials look and feel like:

clay   chalk   marble   sand
slate   granite   sandstone

3 Explain the difference between 'earth' and 'The Earth'.

4 What is the difference between 'sandy soil' and 'peaty soil'?

5 What are the three main types of rock?

6 What are the two different types of weathering?

7 When water freezes it expands, and this is why rocks can split apart. Why could freezing water be a problem at home?

8 What causes 'onion skin weathering'?

9 Make three drawings to show the effect of plant roots. Picture A should show soil in a crack in a rock. Picture B has a seed germinating in it. Picture C has the plant roots forcing the crack wider.

10 Why is rain slightly acidic?

11 Write a word equation for the reaction between an acid and an alkali.

12 Why is limestone attacked more than other types of rock?

13 Put the garden statues in date order starting with the oldest one. The dates are: 1789, 1852, 1906, 1979.

14 When any area gets flooded, the rivers widen and slow down. Explain how people's houses and gardens get mud in them when flooding takes place.

15 Ross Travis explored an uninhabited land and made a map of his survey results.

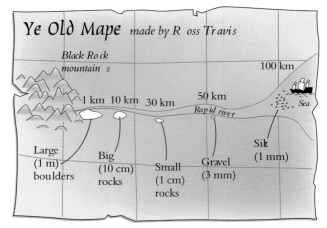

Ye Old Mape *made by R oss Tr avis*

Black Ro ck mountain s

100 km

1 km 10 km 30 km 50 km

Rapid river

Sea

Silt (1 mm)

Large (1 m) boulders

Big (10 cm) rocks

Small (1 cm) rocks

Gravel (3 mm)

He was interested in how far the rock particles from the Black Rock Mountains were carried by the Rapid River.

a) Turn his results into a table.

b) Use the table to make a graph or chart that shows how far the different-sized particles got carried.

c) Prospectors know that gold is often found mixed with 5 mm sized particles of rock. Use your chart to estimate where the prospectors should start to search for gold.

6.3 Chemistry and the environment

Acids in the air

Rain is naturally acidic. It always has been. The rain that fell on the people who lived in Iron Age huts had dissolved some carbon dioxide from the atmosphere to make it weakly acidic.

During the last 200 years the problem has got much worse. Pollutants have made rainfall more strongly acidic. Acid rain attacks marble and decorative stonework. Worse still, it kills vegetation and runs off into lakes where it kills the water life.

When fuels get burned to produce electricity, the sulphur atoms in the fuels react with oxygen from the air to become sulphur dioxide. Sulphur dioxide dissolves in rain to make sulphuric acid.

Petrol and diesel fuel is burned at high pressure in car engines. This produces oxides of nitrogen. These oxides are often called NO_x. These dissolve in rain to make nitric acid.

Figure 1 Lime spraying is used to counteract acid rain because it is alkaline in solution. Lime is the compound calcium oxide.

Plants and rock

Figure 2 Soil is only about 10 m thick.

Different soils have different pH values. The pH of the soil affects which plants can grow in that soil. Most soils have a pH of between 6.0 and 7.0. The soil is weakly acidic because roots absorb nutrient ions from the soil and transfer hydrogen ions back to the soil to preserve a balance. If the soil is too acid, it stops the bacteria releasing nutrients into the soil.

Rock wear

Smooth hard rock looks very beautiful, but rocks wear away very slowly.

You don't notice any change over a month. After ten years, however, you may see the surface begin to become pitted. Then small plants can get a hold and begin the destruction of the rock. Roots widen the little pits and freeze/thaw processes makes cracks bigger.

The outer layer of the rock is heated and flakes away from the cold rock underneath. Small fragments of rock will be carried away by the rain. Eventually the beautiful smooth rock becomes rough, worn and damaged.

What can wear away solid rock?

- The **Sun** – heating, expansion and contraction causes rock to flake.

- **Frost** – gets into cracks, condenses, and then expands as it turns to ice. This splits the rock up.

- **Plants** – their roots continue the damage caused by frost.

Figure 3 What has caused these rocks to look this way?

- The **rain** – makes streams that gradually wear the rock away by washing fragments downstream.

- But most of all **chemicals** in the environment react with the minerals in the rocks to break it down.

Acids and rocks

Acids get at rocks from everywhere!

- Plant roots: put acid particles in the soil.

- Rain: contains dissolved carbon dioxide which makes it weakly acidic.

- Pollution: adds considerably to acidity in the atmosphere. Nitric acid from car exhausts and sulphuric acid from burning fossil fuels are the major sources.

Rocks contain many 'basic' minerals in their mixture of materials. A 'base' in chemistry is a material that neutralises an acid. The acids in the environment dissolve the grains of the 'basic' minerals out of the rock, leaving the rock weakened and more easily eroded. This can be a significant problem when the rock is used for building materials or for decoration.

Acid rain attacks rocks. Acid rain is caused by burning fossil fuels.

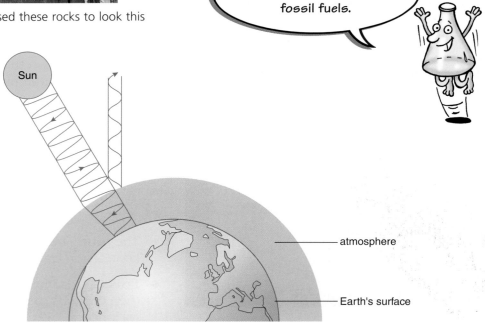

Figure 4 When energy from the Sun reaches the Earth, 30% is reflected back into space, 20% is absorbed by the atmosphere and 50% is absorbed by the surface of the Earth.

Global greenhouse

Figure 5 The most significant greenhouse gas is carbon dioxide. Natural and industrial processes both put carbon dioxide into the atmosphere and take it out. Slash and burn of rainforests (top) and volcanic eruptions (bottom) both add carbon dioxide to the atmosphere.

Global warming will cause:

- higher temperatures (2° to 5°C higher) during the next century
- melting of ice masses at the North and South Poles
- a rise in sea level (of between 20 and 30 cm)
- more flooding of low-lying land
- more violent weather
- more cloud cover and heavy rain

- changes in sea currents
- deserts to move further north
- more storms, hurricanes and floods causing human suffering
- changing crop patterns
- changes in food webs and possible extinction of some species.

Carbon dioxide into the atmosphere	Carbon dioxide out of the atmosphere
burning fossil fuels	photosynthesis and growth in forests and jungles
animal respiration	photosynthesis and growth of sea plankton
rotting vegetation	
burning forests to create farmland	
volcanic eruptions	

Table 3 Inputs and outputs of carbon dioxide

Global warming is melting the ice caps and making weather more violent.

A tale of two ozones

The high atmosphere

Manufactured chemicals (CFCs) from fridges and aerosol sprays, drift up to the stratosphere (between 20 and 50 km above the Earth) and destroy the ozone molecules there. The ozone molecules do a useful job absorbing harmful ultraviolet (UV) radiation. Table 4 shows some of the harmful effects of ultraviolet radiation.

Without the ozone layer, life may never have evolved as we know it now.

Type of radiation	Ultraviolet A	Ultraviolet B	Ultraviolet C
	(longest wavelength)	(medium wavelength)	(shortest wavelength)
Harm rating	Least harmful	Does considerable damage	Lethal
Effect	Tans skin. Can cause damage if skin is exposed for too long.	Burns and ages skin. Causes skin cancers and eye damage (cataracts). Kills plankton in the seas.	Kills small organisms. Damages DNA rapidly; causes skin cancer and eye damage.
Absorption by atmosphere	Gets through ozone layer and oxygen easily.	Absorbed by ozone – not affected by oxygen.	Mostly absorbed by oxygen and remaining ozone in the air.
Precautions	Not a problem, use suntan cream.	Use total sunblock and cover up with long-sleeved clothes.	Not yet a problem.

Table 4   Types of ultraviolet radiation

Figure 6   Bright sun and traffic add up to poison.

Streetcar poisoning: ozone at ground level

- Car engines burn fuel at high pressures.

- The exhaust gases contain NO_x.

- Oxygen (O_2) in the air gets changed into ozone (O_3) when it is combined with the unburned hydrocarbons and oxides of nitrogen (NO_x) and there is strong sunlight.

- The reaction is slow and often the reacting air mass drifts away from the town centre into residential areas.

- If people breathe in the ozone that is produced, it reacts with the blood and prevents it from carrying oxygen.

- Because of this, people's brains don't get enough oxygen. Your brain uses up one-fifth of the oxygen you breathe in.

The atoms from all the fuel we burn end up added to the atmosphere.

Revision

1   Create a snakes and ladders game!

The section is about sources of pollution (the snakes) and how people can prevent the pollution happening (ladders).

Instructions

a) Draw an 8×8 grid like a chessboard on a piece of A3 paper.

b) Use these eight 'snake' ideas:
- Acid rain
- Global warming
- Greenhouse gases
- $2 \times$ effects of climate change
- Ozone layer damage
- UV radiation
- NO_x in city centres

c) Make eight snakes of different lengths to fit on your board game.

d) Each snake should have an explanation round the edge of the board explaining why it is a 'problem'.
- Make eight 'ladders' that are the solution to the eight 'snakes' problems, these should have an explanation as well.
- Fit your snakes and ladders on to your grid to make the game.
- Get a dice and two player tokens. Play the game with a partner.

Questions

1 Draw a diagram to show where the pollution in acid rain comes from.

2 Write word equations for the formation of the acid rain compounds.

3 Catalytic converters on cars turn NO_x back into nitrogen gas. Explain why this reduces acid rain.

4 How could acid rain be prevented in the following places?

a) at the power station

b) where it falls to the ground.

5 Why are acids so harmful to rocks?

6 Why should a bridge over a polluted river *not* be built of limestone?

7 Why is acid rain harmful to rocks like granite that are normally weathered very slowly?

8 What causes the greenhouse effect?

9 Name two gases that contribute to the greenhouse effect.

10 Where do these gases come from?

11 How is human activity making global warming more of a problem?

12 Name three effects of global warming on human life.

13 Use the information in the table below to plot two graphs.

Thousands of years ago	CO_2 in atmosphere (parts per million)	Temp compared to now (°C)
160	200	−9
140	300	0
120	280	−2
100	240	−5
80	230	−5
60	220	−7
40	200	−8
20	200	−9
0	355	0

a) Graph A should be of the amount of carbon dioxide in the atmosphere (*y*-axis) against thousands of years ago (*x*-axis).

b) Graph B should be average temperature (*y*-axis) against thousands of years ago (*x*-axis).

c) Do both the graphs show the same trend?

d) What is the relationship between the amount of CO_2 in the atmosphere and the average temperature?

14 Copy (or get a photocopy of) the rock cycle diagram on page 99 and add these labels to it:

magma   igneous   sedimentary metamorphic   weathering uplift   settling   cementation volcano   melting rock

15 Use these clues to fill in the grid and find the missing word:

a) Tiny _____ from car engines.

b) Atmosphere gas damaged by CFCs.

c) Acid gases cause this.

d) Harmless, mainly water droplets.

e) The sea is polluted by _____ spills.

f) _____ cancer can be caused by strong UV rays.

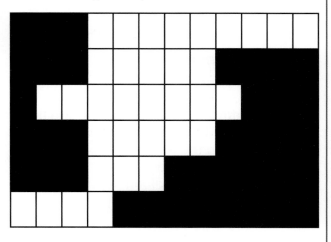

CHAPTER 7

Energy and electricity

7.1 Energy and fuels

Temperature changes

Temperature is something that changes. It is also something we can measure. It is a **variable**.

When we say the temperature of an oven is 180 °C, the number is 180 and the unit is °C, which stands for **degrees Celsius**.

Measuring temperature

We use **thermometers** to measure temperature. One kind of thermometer is a glass tube with a bulb at one end. Inside the bulb is a liquid. This is usually alcohol or **mercury**. When the temperature changes, the liquid expands and spreads along the tube. The tube has markings along the outside, called a **scale**.

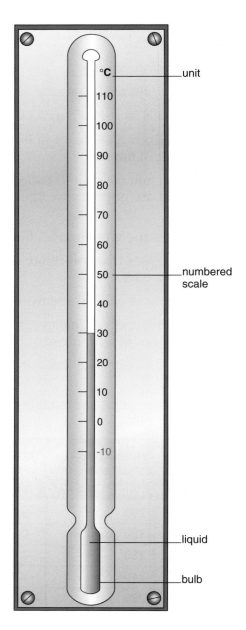

Figure 1   A liquid thermometer

Energy from the Sun

Plants need energy so that they can grow. People need energy to grow, to move and to keep warm.

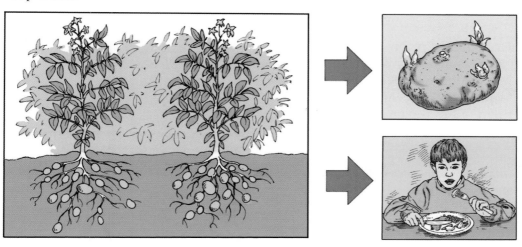

Figure 2   A potato under the ground provides fuel for a new plant to grow. Potatoes also provide energy **resources** for people. They are a kind of fuel for our bodies.

Figure 3   The Sun is the source of our energy resources

- In some villages and homes **solar cells** provide the main energy supply. They provide electricity like batteries do. But they only work when light is shining on them. The light provides the energy to make them work.

- Leaves absorb light from the Sun and gain energy. **Photosynthesis** is the name we give to the way plants do this to build up their energy stores.

- Plants provide the energy that animals need to live and grow.

- Food is an energy resource provided by light from the Sun.

- Trees use sunlight energy to grow. Fuel made from material that has been alive, like trees, is called a **biomass** energy resource.

- In some places in forests and swamps, layers of dead trees and other plants build up. Eventually, the layers might be buried by mud or sand. Coalminers dig out coal that was formed from layers of dead plants that were buried millions of years ago. Coal is a **fossil fuel**.

- Fossil fuels are the remains of plants and animals that lived in the sunshine millions of years ago. These remains have been buried in rock and preserved. We use rigs and coalmines to get them out of the ground.

- The energy of the Sun also creates winds. We can use **wind generators** to provide electricity.

Electric choices

We can use different energy resources to generate electricity. Some of the resources are **renewable**, some are not.

Energy source for generating electricity		Renewable or non-renewable?	Advantage	Disadvantage
Coal	**Coal** is a fossil fuel. Burning coal produces steam to generate electricity in power stations.	Non-renewable	Cheap to run	Acid rain and global warming
Oil	**Oil** is a fossil fuel. Burning oil produces steam to generate electricity.	Non-renewable	Cheap to run	Acid rain and global warming
Gas	**Gas** is a fossil fuel. Burning gas produces steam to generate electricity.	Non-renewable	Very cheap to run	Global warming
Nuclear		Non-renewable	Cheap to run	Long-term danger of waste leaking into the environment. Catastrophic accidents
Hydro-electric	Flowing water turns turbines	Renewable	No fuel costs	Very expensive to build. Destroys countryside
Wind	Energy from moving air used to turn wind turbines and generators.	Renewable	No fuel costs	Takes up a lot of space: noisy and ugly. Unreliable supply
Solar	Energy straight from the Sun.	Renewable	Can be installed anywhere. No fuel costs	Expensive to install. Only works during the day
Biomass	Plant and animal waste material, including dead plants and sewage. Burning biomass produces direct heating or steam to generate electricity.	Renewable	Sometimes cheap	Hard to grow enough

Table 1   Renewable and non-renewable energy sources

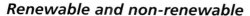

Renewable and non-renewable

Electricity is generated in power stations. Most power stations burn a lot of fuel – usually coal, oil or gas. These fuels come from under the ground. They are fossil fuels.

One day the fossil fuels under the ground will all be used up and there is no way to replace them. They are **non-renewable**. Also, burning fuels produces pollution. Gases go into the atmosphere where they can do harm.

Some energy resources are renewable. They will not run out. As long as the Sun shines there will be winds in the Earth's atmosphere. Energy resources like wind don't pollute the atmosphere.

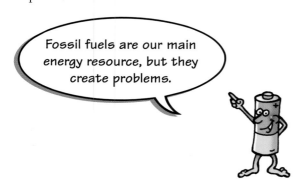

Fossil fuels are our main energy resource, but they create problems.

Fossil fuels produce pollution when we burn them. In cities they can create smoky fog called **smog**. They can damage the countryside by making **acid rain**. Burning fossil fuels also produces a lot of **carbon dioxide**. This goes into the Earth's atmosphere – the air that surrounds the planet. The change in the atmosphere makes the Earth warmer, causing **global climate change**. This will go on for as long as we burn fossil fuels. We don't know what the final results will be.

None of the ways of generating electricity is perfect. Different generating methods should be compared for:

- how much they cost to build and run
- how reliable the supply is
- how much they damage the environment.

Fuels

We can measure the energy values of different fuels in **megajoules** per kilogram.

Fuels provide energy when they burn. They heat their surroundings. We can use the heating effect to do work for us. In a car engine, air and a little bit of fuel get so hot that there is a small explosion. The explosion pushes a piston and that is what makes the wheels go round.

Different fuels have different energy values. We can measure the amount, or mass, of fuel in grams or kilograms. A kilogram is 1000 grams.

Fuel	Energy value in megajoules per kilogram
hydrogen	140
methane	52
petrol	48
coal	35
butter	34
sugar	17
wood	13

Table 2 Energy values of some common fuels

The unit of energy is a **joule**, or J for short. Mega means a million of something, so a megajoule is a million joules. A kilogram of coal provides 35 megajoules of energy.

Hodder Science Summary Book

Revision

1 Match each word from list A with its partner in list B.

List A	List B
temperature	unit
degrees celsius	scale
alcohol	variable
thermometer	mercury

2 Design a chart to show the benefits and problems of using fossil fuels. Here is one idea to help you start.

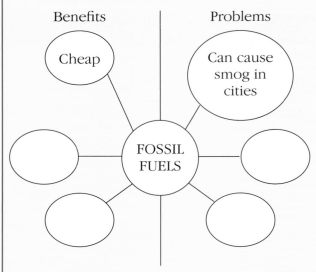

Benefits | Problems

Cheap

Can cause smog in cities

FOSSIL FUELS

Do similar charts for:

● wind energy resources

● nuclear energy resources

● solar energy resources.

Questions

1 What do people's bodies need energy for?

2 Where can people get energy from for their bodies?

3 What unit do we use for measuring temperature?

4 What measuring instrument do we use for measuring temperature?

5 What happens to the liquid in a thermometer when the temperature gets higher?

6 a) Where does a cow get its energy from?

   b) Where do you get your energy from?

7 a) Make a list of as many different energy resources as you can. Here are two to get you started: food, coal.

   b) Can you think of any energy resources that are not created by sunlight?

8 How would you cope without electricity? Write down three things that you would have to give up.

9 Are we being selfish in using up fossil fuels now and not leaving them for future generations of people? Give your opinion.

10 Are we being selfish in burning fossil fuels and changing the atmosphere, when we don't know what effects this will have on the future of the world climate?

11 Which of the fuels in Table 2 can you use for your body?

12 Make a bar chart to show the energy values of different fuels. If you can, use a computer to help you with this.

13 Which fuel in Table 2 has the highest energy value?

7.2 Electric circuits

Key Words

battery	amp
energy	resistance
circuit	parallel
switch	volts
current	cell
heater	voltage
circuit symbol	mains
component	fuse
series	filament
ammeter	

Circuits and symbols

A **battery** or electric cell can supply **energy** to a **circuit**. The circuit has a loop of wire. It has circuit **components** such as lamps. The loop should go from one battery terminal all the way back to the other battery terminal again.

Most circuits have **switches** to control them. We can use special **circuit symbols** for batteries, switches and other components.

Part of circuit (component)	Symbol
Battery or cell	
Switch	
Heater or resistor	

Table 1　Some common circuit symbols

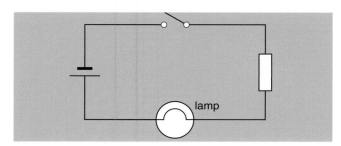

Figure 1　A circuit with a battery, heater wire, switch, lamp and connecting wires

Electricity and energy transfer

An electric **current** in the heater wire makes it warm. The wire spreads the energy into the surroundings.

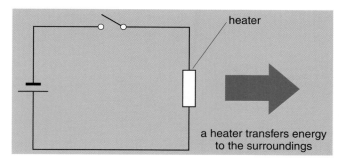

heater

a heater transfers energy to the surroundings

Figure 2　Lamps and heaters transfer energy into the surroundings when they carry a current

Current control

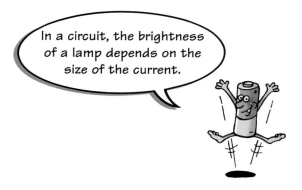

In a circuit, the brightness of a lamp depends on the size of the current.

The **current** measures the electrical flow around the circuit.

You can use an **ammeter** to measure the current in a circuit. We measure current in **amps**.

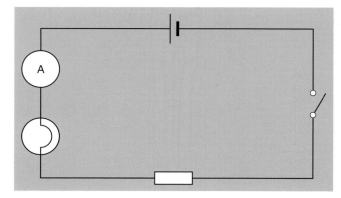

Figure 3　The ammeter goes into the circuit so that the current flows through it. The bigger the current, the further the needle moves along the numbered scale.

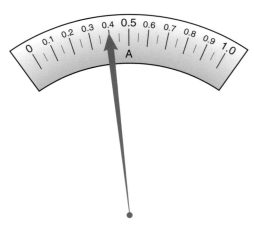

Figure 4 This ammeter scale is numbered 0 to 1.0 A. 'A' stands for amps. The reading on the ammeter is 0.40 A.

> A single-loop circuit is called a **series circuit**. All the components come one after the other, like a series of TV programmes.

Different circuits

Figures 5 and 6 show some other kinds of circuits.

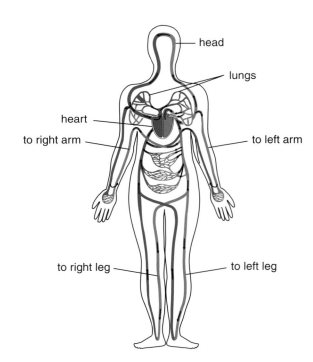

Figure 5 Inside your body there is a current of blood. Your heart is the pump that keeps the current going. It is a complicated circuit, with lots of branches

Figure 6 The boiler, pump, pipes and radiators are components in a central heating circuit. There is a current of hot water all around the circuit

> In an electric circuit you could think of a battery as a pump. The wires are a bit like tubes or pipes.

Components and currents

Components **resist** current. They have **resistance**. The more resistance they have, the more difficult it is for current to flow. When a component's resistance changes, the current changes.

Series and parallel

> In a single loop (series) circuit, the current is the same everywhere.

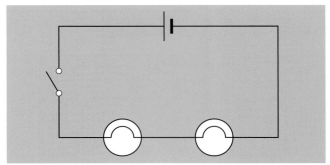

Figure 7 These lamps are connected one after the other – **in series**. These two lamps **resist** current *more* strongly than just one lamp. There is *less* current in this circuit than there would be in the circuit with the same battery but only one lamp

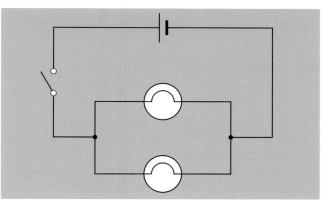

Figure 8 These lamps are connected side by side – **in parallel**. The current has a 'choice' of two routes through the circuit. There is *more* current in this circuit than there would be with the same battery and only one lamp. The two lamps in parallel have *less* resistance than just one lamp

Switches and lamps in parallel

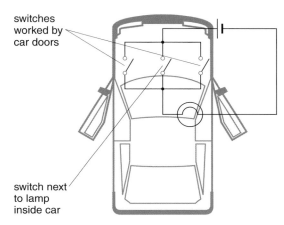

switches worked by car doors

switch next to lamp inside car

Figure 9 This is a circuit for the light that comes on inside a car when you open the front doors. It has three switches – one in each door and one next to the light itself. Any one of the switches will switch the light on. The switches are connected **in parallel**

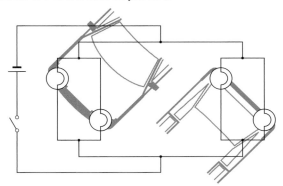

Figure 10 This is a circuit for a car's sidelights. There is only one switch, but there are four lamps. The lamps are connected in parallel. Each one is connected to the terminals of the battery through the switch. A large current flows through the switch when it is 'on' or 'closed'

Measuring current in series and parallel circuits

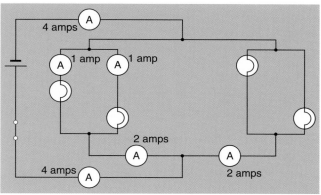

4 amps
A 1 amp A 1 amp
2 amps
4 amps
A
2 amps

Figure 11 In this circuit the ammeters show that the current is split four ways to flow through the lamps

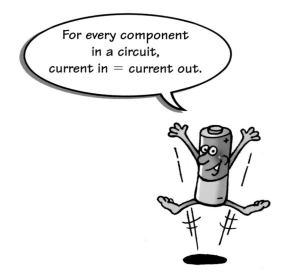

For every component in a circuit, current in = current out.

Lamps and fuses

Strong currents in the thin wires inside a light bulb make the wires white hot. The wires are called **filaments**.

A fuse is a deliberate weak point in a circuit.

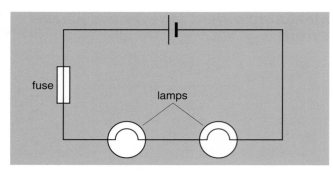

Figure 12   If the current in the lamps of a car is too big, then the filaments could get too hot and melt. To prevent this the car's circuit may contain a **fuse**. A fuse is a small length of thin wire, usually inside a little tube. If the current gets too big the fuse will melt. Then no more current flows, and the lights go out. The fuse is cheap and easy to replace but protects expensive components such as lamps

Electrical supplies

Figure 13   These objects are **cells**. In everyday language we call them **batteries**. A battery is really a number of cells working together to push current around a circuit

The size of a current in a circuit depends on two things:

- What is in the circuit, for example, how many lamps, what kind of lamp and how they are connected.

- The number of cells and the voltage they work at.

Cell measurements

Every cell or battery has a measurement written on it. The unit of the measurement is written as V, which stands for **volts**. A battery's voltage measures the difference between its positive and negative terminals. A cell for a torch might be a 1.5 volt cell. A car battery has a higher **voltage** – usually 12 volts.

Electricity at home

The **mains** electricity in your home is not driven by cells or batteries, but usually by large generators in power stations. The voltage of the mains supply in your house is 230 volts. This is a big voltage, and it can easily produce big currents. If your body becomes part of a mains circuit then the 230 volts can drive a big and dangerous current through your body.

Revision

1   Draw a big circuit. Use the keywords list to add labels to your circuit. Use as many of the key words as you can. Here is part of a circuit with some labels, to help you get started.

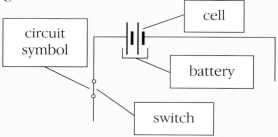

2   Make a list of differences between a circuit that uses a battery and a circuit that uses mains electricity.

3   In a circuit with a lamp, adding an extra lamp in series with the first one *increases* resistance. But adding an extra lamp in parallel with the first one *decreases* the resistance. Can you explain why?

Questions

1 Draw symbols for:

  a) a battery

  b) a lamp

  c) a circuit with a battery and a lamp.

2 Which of these are designed to transfer energy:

  a) a battery

  b) a heater wire

  c) a connecting wire?

3 In what ways is an electric circuit like the blood circuit in your body? In what ways is it different?

4 What happens to the current if the components in a circuit change so that they resist current more?

5 What happens to the current if more lamps are added in series in a circuit?

6 What happens to the current if more lamps are added in parallel with each other?

7 What is the unit for measuring current?

8 Sketch a circuit diagram for a car courtesy light which has switches connected in series. Remember that two switches are operated by the doors. What would you have to do to make the light come on?

9 Predict the measurements on the ammeters marked X in each of these circuits.

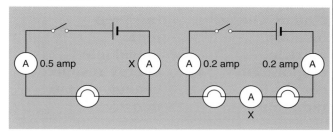

10 Match up these lists:

  230 volts   car battery

  12 volts   torch cell

  1.5 volts   mains electricity in homes

11 Which of these increase the current in a circuit and which decrease it?

  a) adding more lamps in series

  b) adding more lamps in parallel

  c) adding more cells in series.

7.3 Energy transfers

Key Words

energy transfer	conduction
climate change	infra-red
insulate	joule
particle	megajoule
evaporation	energy resource
convection	change of state
radiation	density

Temperature difference and energy transfer

Energy transfers into and out of objects, depending on the temperature difference between them and their surroundings.

Figure 1 Whenever the letterbox is at a higher temperature than its surroundings, energy transfers away from it. When it is cooler than its surroundings, energy transfers into it.

> When the temperatures of the letterbox and its surroundings are the same then there is no overall energy transfer.

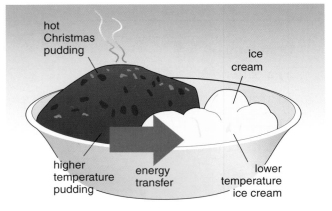

Figure 2 The arrow shows the overall energy transfer. When there is a temperature difference between the objects in contact, one gains energy while the other loses it.

> The hot pudding loses energy. Its temperature goes down.

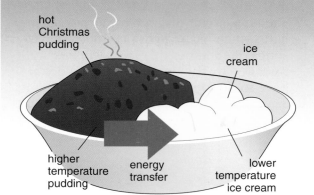

Figure 3

> The cold ice cream gains energy. Its temperature rises (and then it starts to melt).

Energy transfer and change of state

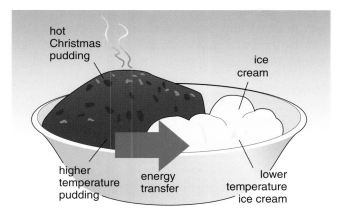

Figure 4 An object that gains energy usually increases in temperature, but not always. While the ice cream is melting its temperature doesn't change. Melting is a change of state, from solid to liquid. (Boiling is another change of state, from liquid to gas.) The energy that the ice cream is receiving from the hot pudding is melting it instead of raising its temperature.

Warm bodies in cold places

Human bodies are usually warmer than their surroundings. They transfer energy to their surroundings. The energy must be replaced or body temperature will fall.

The bigger the difference between our body temperature and the temperature around us, the faster the energy flows away from our body. When the temperature of the surroundings is very low, the energy can transfer out very quickly.

We can wear insulating clothing to slow down **energy transfers** from our body. We can also replace the energy that we lose.

To replace energy we eat food.

Figure 5 Energy stores can replace the energy that transfers out from a human body into the cold world outside.

Figure 6 Early explorers, like the man on the left, had poor food and poor clothing. Modern scientists like the person on the right carry good energy stores, like chocolate, and wear clothing that insulates very well to reduce energy transfer.

Different energy transfers

Energy moves or transfers between different materials which are at different temperatures in different ways.

The different energy transfers are convection, evaporation, conduction and radiation.

Convection

One way to transfer heat from place to place is to move hot material from place to place. A hot air balloon provides an example of hot material floating naturally above cool material. The hot air carries its energy with it. It doesn't just happen in air. In liquids like water, hot parts of the liquid rise above cooler parts of the liquid. Transfer of energy by natural movement of gas or liquid is called **convection**.

Figure 7 The air inside this balloon is hotter than the air outside it. The air in the balloon has expanded. Its particles are further apart than the particles in the air outside. Their density is less. This makes the hot air float in the surrounding cool air and it takes the whole balloon with it.

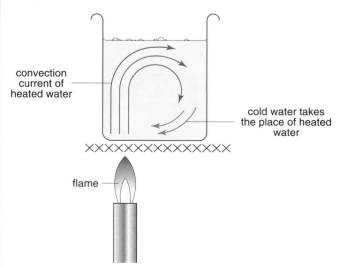

convection current of heated water

cold water takes the place of heated water

flame

Figure 8 A convection current in a liquid

Evaporation

A liquid can **evaporate** into the air around it. Its particles don't stay together any more, but mix with the air. When they evaporate, they take some energy with them. Sweat is a liquid that evaporates into the air and transfers energy in the process. The faster your sweat evaporates, the colder you feel.

Conduction

We know that materials are made of **particles**. Transfer of energy by colliding or interacting particles is called **conduction**.

In gases, fast particles with a lot of energy can bounce off other particles and transfer energy to them. But because the particles are far apart in a gas, there aren't that many collisions. There aren't many opportunities for particles to transfer energy to each other. Gases are not very good at transferring energy by conduction.

In solids, the particles are close together and there are strong forces between them. Energy can transfer quickly from particle to particle. Solids are much better than gases at conducting energy.

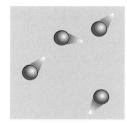

particles in a gas

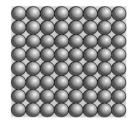

particles in a solid

Figure 9 In solids there are more opportunities for particles to interact.

Radiation

The filament inside a light bulb is so hot that it glows white. It radiates energy to its surroundings. Cooler objects than light bulbs also radiate energy. We call it infra-red radiation.

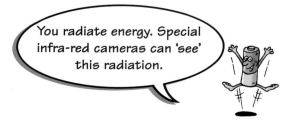

You radiate energy. Special infra-red cameras can 'see' this radiation.

Black objects radiate energy more quickly than silver ones.

Paying the bill for warmth

Warm houses transfer energy into their cooler surroundings. The energy must be replaced. We use many different energy resources for this.

We can burn a gas fire or a coal fire. We can use heaters that run on electricity that is generated in power stations. Central heating might run on oil or natural gas or by using electricity. All of these energy resources cost money, and they all produce pollution.

Previous Bill Balance			0.00	
Total Payments Received			0.00	
Balance Brought Forward			0.00	
Present Gas Charges			51.98	
VAT on present charges @ 5%			2.59	
		Total	54.57	

How your bill is calculated

METER READING PERIOD: 19 May 2008 to 31 May 2008
ODP

Meter Serial Number	METER READINGS		GAS USED				kWh Cost	Charge £
	Present	Previous	Calorific Value MJ/m3	100's Cubic Feet	Cubic Metres	kWh		
0000730	4754 E	4734 E	38.20	20.45	57.88	614	1.165	7.15

Daily Standing Charge 12 days @ 7.26p per day | | | | | | | | 0.87

Figure 10 To keep our houses warm takes megajoules of energy every week. Joules and megajoules are units of energy

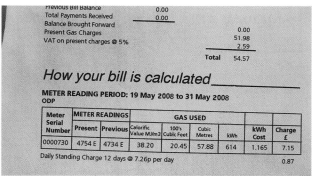

A megajoule is a million joules.

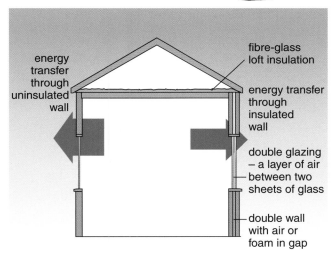

energy transfer through uninsulated wall

fibre-glass loft insulation

energy transfer through insulated wall

double glazing – a layer of air between two sheets of glass

double wall with air or foam in gap

Figure 11 In winter it is cold outside and warmer inside. The temperature difference makes energy transfer rapidly outwards. Energy flows through the walls, windows and roof. We can double glaze our windows, and we can put layers of fibre-glass wool in the loft to reduce the energy flow. Fibre glass is a good thermal insulator

Questions

1 Why does a hot drink, like hot tea, cool down but you don't?

2 What would happen to the temperature of a letterbox when it snows if:

  a) the snow is warmer than the letterbox is to start with?

  b) the snow is colder than the letterbox is to start with?

3 When you run hot water and cold water into a bath, which water warms up and which water cools down?

4 Sketch energy transfer diagrams, with arrows to show the energy flow for:

  a) an ice cube floating in a glass of lemonade

  b) an iceberg that floats from cold water into warmer water

  c) a pile of cold oven chips when you put them into a hot oven

  d) a bottle of warm milk that has just been moved from a warm room into a fridge.

5 What does 'insulation' mean?

6 Explain:

  a) why you lose energy more quickly when swimming in the sea than when in a hot bath

  b) why cold weather makes you hungry

  c) why heating part of a liquid makes the liquid start to move and causes a convection current.

7 **a)** You heat the bottom of a saucepan on a cooker. The liquid inside the saucepan gets hotter. How does the energy transfer through the saucepan?

  b) You make some toast. How does the energy transfer to the bread?

8 Name one unit of energy.

9 Describe two ways of saving money on heating bills.

10 Explain the advantages of solar energy over other energy resources for heating. What are the disadvantages?

Revision

1 These are some objects and their temperatures.

YOU 37°C

ELECTRICAL HEATER BAR 600°C

SNOWMAN -2°C

MUG OF TEA 60°C

We know that energy will transfer from the electric heater bar to the snowman. That's because of the temperature difference.

Make six similar diagrams, using arrows like the one in Fig 2, to show energy transfer that will take place between all of the possible pairs of the objects.

Predict what would happen to the energy transfers that involve the mug of tea if it were insulated.

The mug of tea gets cold when it transfers energy to its surroundings. But you and the electric heater stay at the same temperature. You and the heater need to replace the energy you transfer out. Where do

a) you

b) the heater

get the energy from?

2 A vacuum flask will keep liquid hot for much longer than an ordinary bottle will. Use your knowledge of convection, evaporation, conduction and radiation to explain how it does this.

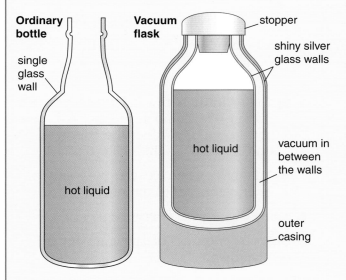

Ordinary bottle

single glass wall

hot liquid

Vacuum flask

stopper

shiny silver glass walls

hot liquid

vacuum in between the walls

outer casing

3 These are some key words. Make a concept map to show which words are closely linked to each other.

temperature   energy transfer   insulate
evaporation   energy   convection
radiation   conduction   joule

Once you have done this, look at the key words list on page 137. Add the rest of the words from the list to your concept map.

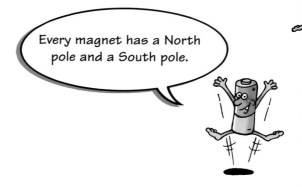

7.4 Magnetism

Key Words	
field	electromagnet
attract	electric current
repel	field lines
north pole	relay
south pole	amplitude
magnetic	amplifier
permanent	loudspeaker
magnet	

> Every magnet has a North pole and a South pole.

Magnetic forces

Sometimes magnets attract and sometimes they repel. They can push and pull each other without touching. The space around a magnet where its force can act is called its magnetic field.

Most materials, like air, water, paper and brick, are not **magnetic**. The most common magnetic materials are iron and steel. Steel is good for making permanent bar **magnets**. Steel magnets keep their magnetism. Compass needles are made of steel.

Patterns of magnetism

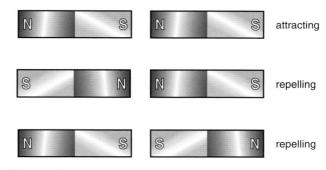

Figure 2   There is a pattern to the way magnets **attract** or **repel**; north poles attract south poles, and south poles attract north poles. Two poles that are *different* always *attract*. Two poles that are the *same* always *repel* each other.

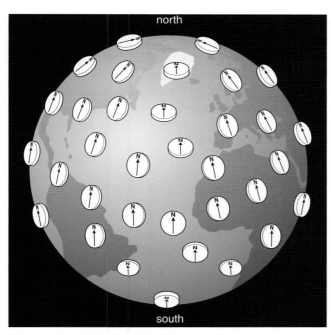

Figure 1   The Earth itself is a very large magnet.

A compass is a small magnet that can swing freely. Compasses all over the Earth point from South to North. So wherever you are you can use a compass to tell which way is North and which way is South.

The end of the compass that points North is called its **north pole**. The end that points South is called its **south pole**. Every magnet has a **north pole** and a **south pole**.

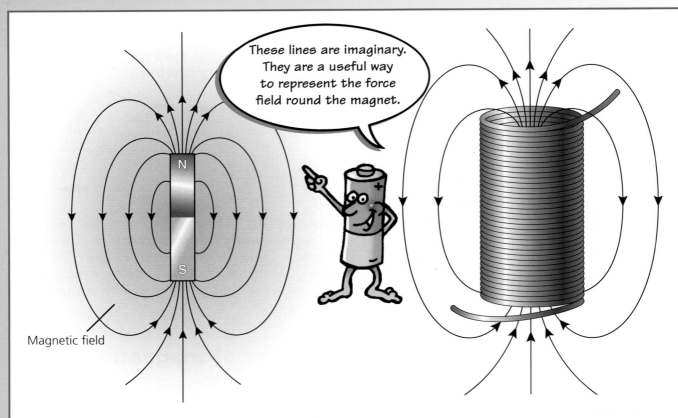

These lines are imaginary. They are a useful way to represent the force field round the magnet.

Magnetic field

Figure 3 You can use little compasses to trace the patterns of magnetic forces that act in the area around a magnet. You end up with a pattern of looping lines. These are called **field** lines, or sometimes lines of force. Arrows on the lines show which way the compass needle points

Figure 4 When an electric current flows in a wire, the space around the wire becomes a magnetic field. If the wire is made into a tight coil it acts as a strong magnet that can be switched on and off. It is called an **electromagnet**. It has a pattern of field lines around it

Look at the patterns of field lines around the electromagnet in Figures 3 and 4.

● The lines are closer together where the field is stronger.

● The lines and arrows show the direction of the force of the field.

Figure 5 Inhabitants of Aberffordd

Power lines

TV presenter: Here in the village of Aberffordd the local doctor, Dr Mair Roberts, has brought attention to a very high rate of cancer amongst local people.

Doctor Roberts: Nobody can be sure what causes it. We've tested the water and that's completely normal. Many people here work on farms and someone suggested that some of the pesticides they use could have harmful effects. Though in similar farming villages there isn't the same high rate of cancer. Another suggestion is that the problem is caused by the high voltage power cables that pass over the village from the power station two miles away.

TV presenter: They look like ordinary power cables.

Doctor Roberts: All power cables carry quite strong electric current, and that means that there are strong magnetic fields all around them.

TV presenter: Are you saying that the magnetic fields in the space around the cables are causing cancer?

Doctor Roberts: We can't say that for sure, and the electricity company say that there's no evidence that magnetism causes cancer.

TV presenter: Is there anything about these particular magnetic fields that could be a problem?

Doctor Roberts: Well, the current in the cables is large, and that makes strong magnetic effects. Also the current isn't steady, but vibrates backwards and forwards 50 times per second. It's alternating current. That means that the magnetic fields are also vibrating, and perhaps the vibrations can affect the complicated chemistry in a human body.

TV presenter: Nobody denies that there's a problem here in Aberffordd, but nobody has any idea about the cause, and still less about what can be done. This is Gita Patel, News at Nine, Aberffordd.

> If the current in a wire varies, then the strength of the magnetic field varies in just the same way.

Bells

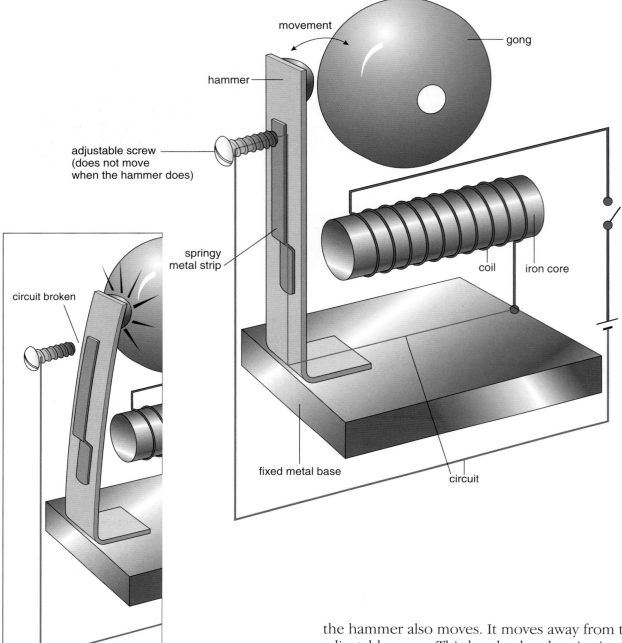

movement

gong

hammer

adjustable screw
(does not move
when the hammer does)

springy
metal strip

coil

iron core

circuit broken

fixed metal base

circuit

Figure 6 How an electric bell works

The electromagnet in an electric bell is a coil of wire. When a current flows in the coil it becomes a magnet. The coil has a core of iron to make the magnetism as strong as possible.

When you switch the bell on the coil attracts the iron of the hammer. The hammer moves and hits the gong. The springy metal strip fixed to the hammer also moves. It moves away from the adjustable screw. This breaks the electric circuit so the current stops and the coil loses its magnetism.

Now there is nothing to attract the hammer across to the gong. It goes back to where it started. Then the springy metal strip again makes contact with the adjustable screw and so the current is switched back on. The current flows in the coil and the whole process starts over again. The hammer dashes backwards and forwards, several times every second.

Loudspeakers

The metal string of an electric guitar does not make a very loud sound. It does not make vibrations with very high amplitude. But the vibrations of the string generate small electric currents in the guitar's circuits. An amplifier makes bigger currents with the same patterns in them. These bigger currents are enough to make a loudspeaker vibrate with high amplitude. Then the quiet guitar is as loud as you want it to be.

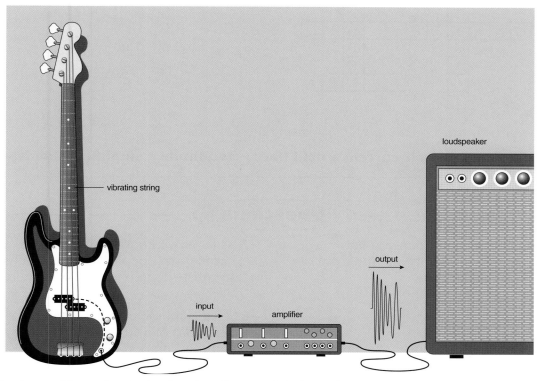

Figure 7   An amplifier makes the loudspeaker vibrate with high amplitude

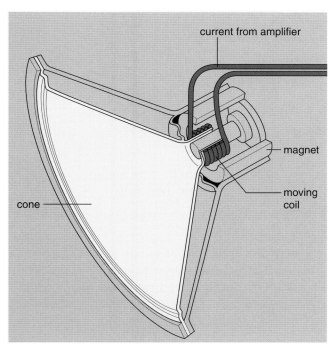

Figure 8   The main components of a loudspeaker

The main parts of a loudspeaker are a cone, a coil and a fixed magnet. The coil is attached to the cone. The electric current from the amplifier flows through the coil and it becomes magnetic. The current varies, and so the force between the coil and the fixed magnet also varies. The coil and the cone vibrate to make vibrations in the surrounding air.

The process of making loud sounds from quiet ones is called amplification.

Revision

1 This is a 'key word' puzzle. Make up a set of clues so that somebody else could use the blank grid to complete the puzzle themselves.

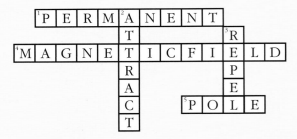

2 Make your own word puzzle, with clues, using these words:

electromagnet   electric current   field lines   amplitude   amplifier   loudspeaker

Questions

1 Write down the things that you know about the force of gravity and the force of magnetism that are:

a) the same

b) different.

2 Draw the shape of the magnetic field around a bar magnet. Add arrows to show the directions of the force.

3 Why would a compass be of no use if you were navigating in space?

4 What effect does:

a) a north pole of a magnet have on another north pole?

b) a north pole of a magnet have on a south pole?

5 **a)** Why is steel good for making compass needles?

b) In what ways is an electromagnet more useful than a permanent steel magnet?

6 **a)** Why are the magnetic fields around power lines strong?

b) Why do the magnetic fields 'vibrate' rapidly?

7 As far as we know, magnetic fields are harmless to people. What research could scientists do to try to find out more about this?

8 What is the difference between the vibrations of a string of an electric guitar and the vibration of the loudspeaker that provides an amplified version of the same note?

9 Describe what each of these does to make a loudspeaker produce sound:

a) amplifier

b) coil

c) fixed magnet

d) cone.

10 **a)** Which of these use electromagnets to make sound:

human voice   TV   radio   piano
electric bell

b) What does an electromagnet do in a loudspeaker?

11 Explain how an electric bell rings continuously and does not make just a single 'ding' of the hammer on the gong.

7.5 Energy and electricity

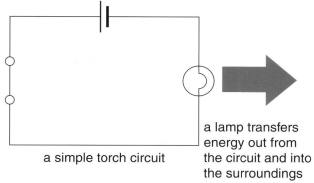

a simple torch circuit

a lamp transfers energy out from the circuit and into the surroundings

Figure 2 The wire in the bulb of a torch gets very hot. It transfers energy to its surroundings. The energy becomes spread out in the large surroundings. The surroundings get a little warmer. Then we say that the energy has **dissipated.**

Energy transfer from circuits

A cell or **battery** has two terminals – one positive and one negative. Electric current flows between the terminals when they are connected together to make an electric circuit.

Circuits can transfer energy by heating and by doing work.

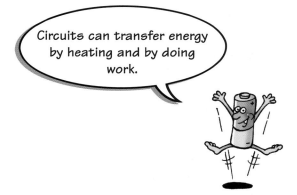

Figure 1 A cell or battery is an energy store. It can transfer energy to a circuit, and the circuit can transfer energy to the surroundings.

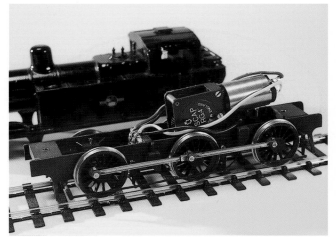

Figure 3 Energy transfer by doing work, and then by heating. The motor in an electric toy transfers energy to the toy to make it move. The motor gets warm and heats the surroundings. The energy dissipates

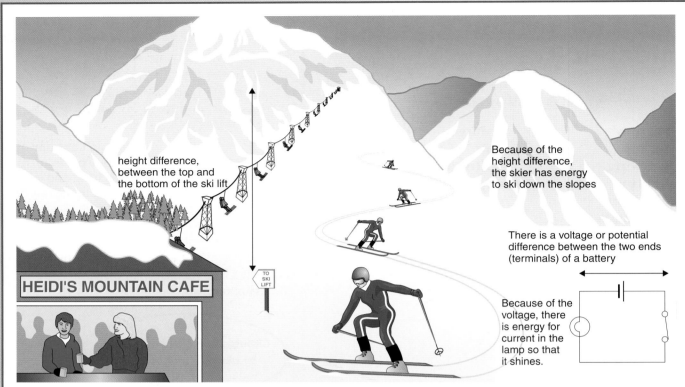

Figure 4 This is a model of an electric circuit. It helps us to think about how a real circuit transfers energy. The ski-lift supplies energy to the skiers. In a simple electric circuit, it is not a ski-lift but a battery that provides the energy.

A ski-slope has a height difference so that the skiers can ski. We measure batteries by their voltage. A battery's voltage is the difference between its positive and negative terminals. It is the difference that makes the current flow.

Skiers can go round and round their circuit, up and down the mountain. A current can go round and round an electric circuit.

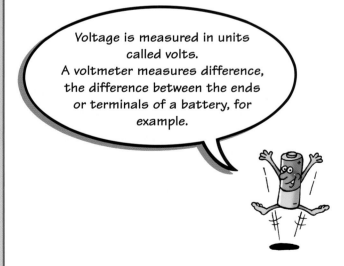

Generating electricity

A power station generator transfers energy from hot steam to a turbine and then a generator, and then to the electric cables that are connected to our homes, schools, shops and factories.

Hydroelectric power stations have turbines and generators that are turned by flowing water

– just like an old water mill but much, much faster. Hydroelectric power stations store water in a high reservoir. The water high in the reservoir has position energy or **potential energy**. Then when the water races down the pipes it has motion energy or **kinetic energy**. The water loses most of its kinetic energy when it turns the turbines. The turbines transfer the energy to the electric generators.

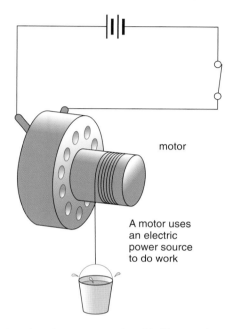

motor

A motor uses an electric power source to do work

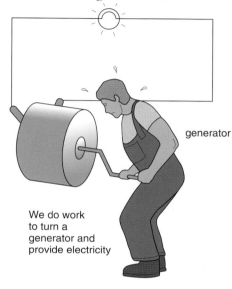

generator

We do work to turn a generator and provide electricity

Figure 5   An electric generator is a bit like an electric motor in reverse. For a generator, a source of energy has to be used to make it turn. That makes a current flow.

Energy rates

Different appliances at home transfer energy at different rates. Appliances that transfer energy quickly are high power appliances. They are expensive to run.

A kettle has a high power rating and transfers energy quickly. It has a strong heating effect.

Figure 6   Power = 2400 watt. Energy cost for 1 hour is *about* 24p.

Hodder Science Summary Book

An electric hair drier has a heater and a motor. It transfers energy to its surroundings by heating. It also transfers energy by doing work and making air move – it gives kinetic energy to the air.

Figure 7   Power = 400 watt. Energy cost for 1 hour is *about* 4p

You can find out the *approximate* hourly cost of running an appliance by dividing its power rating in watts by 100. So the energy supply for a 500 watt computer costs about 5p per hour. A 100 watt lamp would cost about 1p per hour.

Efficiency

We want a vacuum cleaner to do work. We don't want it to heat the room, but the motor does get warm. The energy that the motor transfers by heating is not useful. We can compare the *useful* energy transfer with the *wasted* energy transfer by talking about efficiency. If the vacuum cleaner is 40% efficient then only 40% of the energy that is given to it by the electricity supply is transferred usefully. The other 60% is transferred directly by useless heating.

We could transfer less energy in our homes by using appliances, like fridge-freezers, that have high efficiency. They can provide us with the same benefits but transfer as little energy as possible in the process.

Revision

1   What's the difference between:
- a battery and a cell
- a motor and a generator
- working and heating
- dissipation and efficiency
- current and voltage
- an ammeter and a voltmeter
- a watt and a kilowatt
- an amp and a volt
- potential energy and kinetic energy?

Questions

1   A kettle supplies energy to water to make it hot. If the water cools down again, where has the energy gone to?

2   An electric circuit can make a motor go round. What has happened to all of the energy when the motor has stopped?

3   What is the unit of
   a) electric current?
   b) electric voltage?

4   How does a hair drier transfer energy to its surroundings?

5   Sketch a 400 watt hi-fi and a 1000 watt electric heater. Add arrows to show the flow of energy through the appliances. Show the sizes of the rates of transfer by the sizes (widths) of the arrows you draw.

6   Compare the skiing model with a water circuit model of an electric circuit. Which is more like a real electric circuit? How are the models different to a real electric circuit? Which is more useful for helping you to understand difficult ideas about how electricity works?

CHAPTER 8

Space, force and motion

8.1 Force and motion

> ### Key Words
>
> | | |
> |---|---|
> | metre | unit |
> | kilometre | air resistance |
> | second | balanced |
> | newton | friction |
> | extension | accelerate |
> | gravity | unbalanced |
> | scale | driving force |
> | attract | thrust |
> | repel | drag |
> | weight | upthrust |

Speed, time and distance

Speed, time and distance are quantities that we can link together in a useful pattern.

$$\text{speed} = \frac{\text{distance travelled}}{\text{time taken}}$$

That means that speed is distance traveled divided by time taken.

Figure 1 An Olympic sprinter

We can work out the speed of the sprinter in Figure 1 by dividing the distance by the time.

distance = 100 metres
time = 10 seconds
speed = ?

Speed = distance ÷ time

We replace the words by the numbers

Speed = 100 ÷ 10

Now we do the arithmetic:

Speed = 10 metres per second

We write the **unit** of speed with the answer.

Different kinds of force

There are different kinds of force. The force of **gravity** is a force that attracts. It acts everywhere on Earth.

The force of gravity keeps the Earth and the Moon together. The Earth and the Moon don't touch – the force acts at a distance.

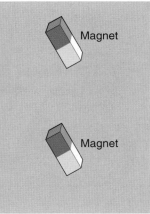

Figure 2 Magnets can attract each other like the Earth and the Moon do. They can also repel each other. The force between magnets is not a force of gravity. It is magnetic force

Stretching force

A force is needed to stretch a spring.

The amount of stretch is sometimes called the **extension** of the spring.

We can use the stretch of a spring to measure force. We need a spring with a hook, and a scale for making the measurements. There is a unit for measuring force, called a **newton**.

Figure 3   We measure force using forcemeters. The bigger the force, the more the spring stretches

Forces of resistance

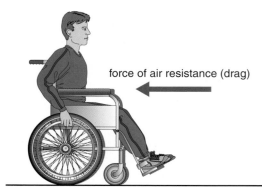

Figure 4   Forces of air resistance are sometimes called **drag** forces. The faster you go through the air, the more resistance you feel. Drag has a slowing down effect

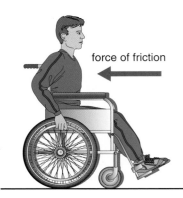

Figure 5   When surfaces touch each other it can be hard for them to slide. It is hard for the wheel to slide against the axle that is holding it – this is friction. Forces of friction are forces of resistance. They have a slowing down effect

Balanced and unbalanced forces

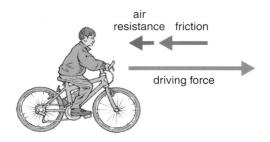

Figure 6   Going faster. There is friction in the moving parts of the bike. But at low speed there isn't much air resistance acting against you. If you exert a big driving force, you will go faster (accelerate)

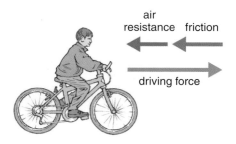

Figure 7   Cruising along. Friction and air resistance provide forces that resist movement. There is more air resistance at high speed. But if your driving force matches the resistive forces, you will keep going at a steady speed. You don't accelerate any more. The forces are balanced

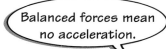

Balanced forces mean no acceleration.

Balanced and unbalanced forces in water

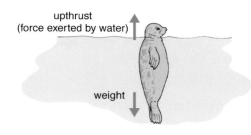

upthrust (force exerted by water)

weight

Figure 10 A seal has a lot of weight, but objects in water also experience an upwards force called **upthrust**. When upthrust balances weight, the motion of an object doesn't change.

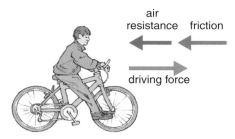

air resistance   friction

driving force

Figure 8 Slowing down. If you make the driving force small then it will not be big enough to balance the friction and air resistance any more. Forces acting against your movement are bigger than the driving force. The forces are unbalanced. You slow down. Slowing down is a kind of acceleration. Speeding up, slowing down and changing direction all involve acceleration.

The forces acting on the seal are balanced.

Unbalanced force always makes you change speed or direction. It always produces acceleration of some kind.

thrust   drag

Figure 11 A dolphin uses its flippers and its strong tail to create a driving force. Another name for driving force is thrust. Water exerts big drag forces. Dolphins need strong muscular forces to create enough thrust to balance the drag

Balancing the force of gravity

Figure 9 Everything accelerates towards the Earth unless there is an upwards force to balance the weight. The weightlifter has to struggle to provide an upward force that is big enough

If the forces are balanced then the dolphin has steady speed.

Hodder Science Summary Book

1 What's the difference between:

- a metre and a kilometre
- a second and a newton
- friction and air resistance
- thrust and drag
- weight and upthrust
- balanced and unbalanced?

Questions

1 Suppose that you walk 4 metres in 2 seconds. Copy and complete the following to work out what your speed would be:

speed =   distance   ÷ time

that's 4 metres divided by 2 seconds

speed = _____ metres ÷ ____seconds

4 divided by 2 is 2

speed = _____ metres per second.

2 A runner in a marathon race covers 42 kilometres in 3 hours. Copy this and fill in the gaps:

speed = _____ travelled ÷ time taken

that's 42 kilometres divided by _____hours

speed = _____ kilometres ÷ _____hours

42 divided by 3 is 14

speed = _____ kilometres per hour.

3 Copy and complete this table by writing 'yes' or 'no' in the spaces:

	Force of gravity	Magnetic force
Can act without touching		
Only provides forces of attraction		
Provides forces of attraction and repulsion		

4 **a)** On a bike, what happens to your speed when the forces acting on you are balanced?

b) What happens when the driving force is bigger than the resistive forces?

5 Copy and complete this table of information:

Moving object	Driving force	Forces resisting motion	Forces balanced or unbalanced	Speed – steady, increasing or decreasing
bird flying at steady speed	force between wings and air	air resistance		steady
apple falling from tree	gravity	air resistance	unbalanced	
sports bag sliding across floor	none (after it's released)	friction		
plane on runway	thrust provided by engines	air resistance, friction		increasing
plane in steady flight				steady

8.2 The Solar System

Key Words

eclipse	planet
Full Moon	day
New Moon	night
ray	spin
shadow	year
atmosphere	tilt
gravity	seasons
Sun	hemisphere
orbit	

Sunlight

The **Sun** is very big but it is a long way from Earth. The light from the Sun takes about 8 minutes to reach the Earth, even though light travels at very high speed.

> If there was a non-stop motorway to the Sun, it would take you more than 100 years to get there.

Rays of light

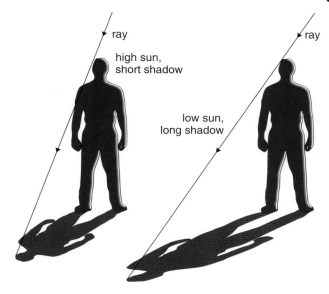

ray

high sun, short shadow

ray

low sun, long shadow

Figure 2   We can make diagrams to show the straight pathways of light. The pathways are called rays

The sunny side of the Moon

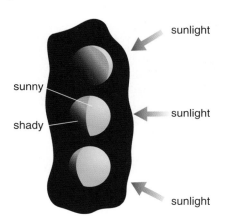

sunlight

sunny

shady

sunlight

sunlight

Figure 3   Sunlight can only shine on half of the Moon at a time. From Earth we see the sunny part. Sometimes we see all of the sunny side of the Moon and then we call it a **Full Moon**. Sometimes we see the shady side of the Moon, and just a thin slice of the sunny side. Then we call it a **New Moon**

Figure 1   Without the sun there would be no light or life on earth

A solar eclipse

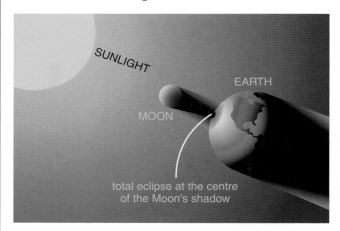

Figure 4   The Earth and the Moon make big shadows. Sometimes the shadow of the Moon falls onto the Earth. It doesn't happen very often. It is called a solar **eclipse**

Figure 5   A solar eclipse as we see it from Earth

During a solar eclipse the Moon is in front of the Sun. We are in the Moon's shadow.

A lunar eclipse happens when the Moon is in the Earth's shadow.

Gravity

Stars and planets pull strongly on all other objects that are near to them. The force is the **force of gravity**.

Figure 6   Only a few animals and a few people have been outside the Earth's **atmosphere** and into space. The first animal to do this was Laika, a Russian dog, in 1957

The atmosphere is a layer of air all around the Earth.

Figure 7   Astronauts escape from the Earth's atmosphere into space. But they *don't* go far enough to escape from the Earth's gravity. Gravity holds them in orbit around the Earth

The Solar System

The Sun is a huge star at the centre of a system of planets called the Solar System. The Sun's strong force of gravity keeps the planets in orbit.

There are no stars other than the Sun anywhere near the Solar System.

In the past, most people guessed that the Sun and the planets and the stars all went around the Earth. They couldn't explain the way that the planets seemed to move in more complicated ways across the sky. Then a Polish monk called Copernicus explained that the Earth could actually *be* a planet itself, and that the Earth and the *other* planets were all going round the Sun.

Earth

Comet

Figure 8   If we could see the Solar System from outside it might look *a bit* like this. The sizes of the planets are exaggerated. In reality the Sun is by far the biggest object in the Solar System. From outside the Solar System, the Earth would be too small to see at all. This picture also shows a comet. A comet is much smaller than a planet

Day and night

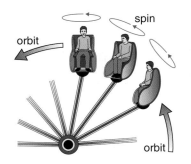

spin

orbit

fairground ride – orbits and spins at the same time

orbit

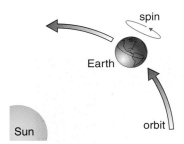

spin

Earth

orbit

Sun

the best ride of all – the Earth orbits and spins at the same time; one orbit every year, one spin every day

Figure 9 We speed round the Sun, and make a complete **orbit** once in every Earth year. At the same time we spin. It takes just one Earth day to make a complete **spin**. It is the spin of the Earth that carries us into light and darkness every day

We take a year for a complete journey around the Sun, and we take a day for one spin. It's the spin that gives us day and night.

Seasons

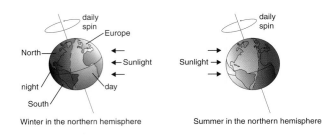

Winter in the northern hemisphere

Summer in the northern hemisphere

Figure 10 The Earth's spin has a tilt. For part of each year, the northern half is tilted towards the Sun. The northern half is called the northern hemisphere. At this time the Sun shines more from overhead and the weather is warmer. This is summer. At the same time the southern half is tilted away from the Sun. There the sunshine is not so strong and it is winter there.

When it's winter in the north it's summer in the south. So Christmas is in summertime in Australia.

Planets

Figure 11   Jupiter is the biggest planet. It is a very different world from our own planet Earth. It is a ball of gas, but because it is so big its gravity is very strong

Mercury	1416	=	1 Mercury day
Venus	5832	=	1 Venus day
Earth	24	=	1 Earth day
Mars	25	=	1 Mars day
Jupiter	10	=	1 Jupiter day
Saturn	10	=	1 Saturn day
Uranus	11	=	1 Uranus day
Neptune	16	=	1 Neptune day
Pluto	6	=	1 Pluto day

Table 2   Time to spin once, in hours

Bigger planets have stronger gravity. The closer you get to a planet, the stronger its gravity gets.

The days would drag on and on if you went to Venus.

Planet data

Mercury	88 Earth days	=	1 Mercury year
Venus	225 Earth days	=	1 Venus year
Earth	365.25 Earth days	=	1 Earth year
Mars	687 Earth days	=	1 Mars year
Jupiter	12 Earth years	=	1 Jupiter year
Saturn	30 Earth years	=	1 Saturn year
Uranus	84 Earth years	=	1 Uranus year
Neptune	165 Earth years	=	1 Neptune year
Pluto	248 Earth years	=	1 Pluto year

Table 1   Length of the planet's year – the time it takes to travel once round the Sun

Mercury	7°
Venus	3°
Earth	24°
Mars	26°
Jupiter	3°
Saturn	27°
Uranus	88°
Neptune	29°
Pluto	50°

Table 3   Tilt of spin

Venus and Jupiter hardly have seasons at all.

1 Look at Figure 8.

Make a list of the ways in which it is not like the Solar System. Why would it be impossible to make a picture of the Solar System that shows the planets and is completely accurate?

2 Explain how movements of the Earth and Moon in the Solar System cause:

- a New Moon

- a Full Moon

- a solar eclipse

- day and night

- seasons.

3 Write down **five** differences between pattern of light and warmth on Earth compared with some other planets.

1 Imagine that you spend a long afternoon in the park. Late in the afternoon you find yourself in the shadow of a tree, even though you've stayed in the same place in the park all day.

a) What happens to the height of the Sun in the sky as the afternoon goes by?

b) What happens to the lengths of the shadows as the afternoon goes by and it becomes evening.

c) What happens to the position of the shadows?

d) You see the Sun go down at 8.20 in the evening. What time did the light that you see leave the Sun?

2 Why do we sometimes see a Full Moon and sometimes see a New Moon?

3 Explain what makes a solar eclipse happen.

4 **a)** What is the Earth's atmosphere?

b) Why do space capsules need to carry an air supply?

5 Why is the gravity of the Moon weaker than the gravity of the Earth?

6 If the Sun is just a star, why does it look much bigger than other stars?

7 Which of the planets is most like Earth in:

a) the time taken to go around the Sun

b) the time taken to spin once

c) the tilt of its spin?

8 **a)** How many times have you been around the Sun?

b) If you'd lived all your life on Jupiter, how many times would you have gone around the Sun? What is your age in Jupiter years?

9 On Venus there isn't much difference between summer and winter. Can you explain why?

8.3 Gravity and space

Balancing gravity

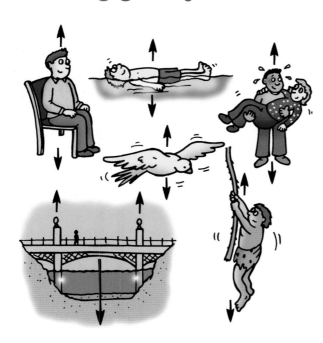

Figure 1   Balancing gravity

Figure 1 shows ways to provide an upwards force to balance **gravity**:

● Sit (or stand) on a seat.

● Float on water.

● Get a friend to carry you.

● Be a bird and let the force of the wind on your wings support you.

● Be a bridge and let the pillars provide the upwards force.

● Be Tarzan and hang from the trees by a vine.

Parachuting – balanced and unbalanced forces

Figure 2   The force of gravity can make a parachutist accelerate downwards – but there's also the force of air resistance that acts upwards. When these forces are in balance, parachutists drift to the ground at a constant speed called **terminal velocity**. They don't accelerate

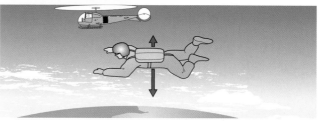

Figure 3   High above the Earth, near the start of a parachute jump gravitational force is pulling down on the parachutist. The force of air resistance acts in the opposite direction. But the parachutist is still only moving slowly, so the force of air resistance is small. The forces are unbalanced. The parachutist accelerates towards the ground.

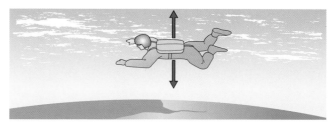

Figure 4   A bit later . . . The parachutist has accelerated. In fact she has gained so much speed that air resistance acting on her has grown as big as the force of gravity. The forces are in balance. Motion is not changing any more. The parachutist falls at a steady speed

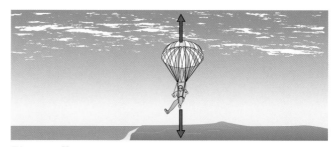

Figure 5   Later still . . . With the parachute open, air resistance can balance the force of gravity while the parachutist falls slowly and steadily

Falling towards the Moon

The Moon is smaller than the Earth so its gravitational pull is weaker, but it is still strong enough to make you accelerate towards the surface. The Moon has no air. There is no air resistance to exert an upwards force.

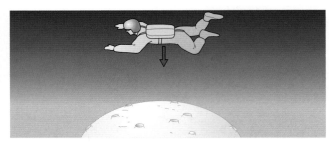

Figure 6 High above the Moon, near the start of a jump gravitational force is pulling down on the parachutist. There is no force of air resistance to balance the force of gravity. The parachutist accelerates downwards all the way to the surface.

Mass and weight on Earth and in deep space

We can measure the mass of a human body, or any kind of body, in kilograms. Whether an astronaut is in space or walking on the Moon, they have exactly the same mass.

We can use grams for the masses of small bodies – a kilogram is a thousand grams. Or we could use tonnes for large bodies – a tonne is a thousand kilograms.

The force of gravity on a body is NOT the same wherever it goes. The strength of the force that a large body like the Earth or the Moon can exert on your body depends on how far away you are. An astronaut floating deep in space, very far from the Earth or any other very large object, experiences no force of gravity at all. We say the astronaut is **weightless**. The force of gravity acting on a body is called its weight.

Because weight is a force it is measured in newtons. In everyday life most people talk about weight measured in kilograms. We need to be more careful with what we say when we talk about space.

Orbit

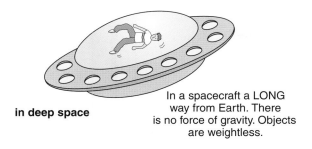

in deep space

In a spacecraft a LONG way from Earth. There is no force of gravity. Objects are weightless.

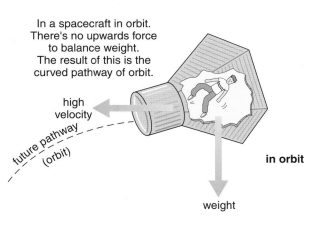

In a spacecraft in orbit. There's no upwards force to balance weight. The result of this is the curved pathway of orbit.

high velocity

future pathway (orbit)

in orbit

weight

on Earth

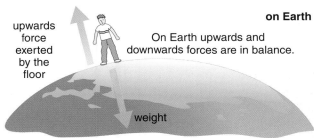

upwards force exerted by the floor

On Earth upwards and downwards forces are in balance.

weight

Figure 7 Forces in space, in orbit and on Earth

On the surface of the Earth, the floor exerts a strong force on you to balance the force of gravity. In deep space there is no force of gravity, and you would float freely in your spacecraft.

In orbit there is a force of gravity. The force makes your motion change – it changes its direction. If you have enough speed you don't get any closer to the Earth, and you stay in orbit.

You and your orbiting spacecraft travel in the same circle. The walls and floor of the spacecraft don't exert any force on you. You *feel* weightless even though gravity is acting.

Isaac Newton and ideas about force

We often think that the natural thing for moving objects to do is to slow down and stop. But Isaac **Newton** worked on **Galileo's** idea that the natural thing for moving objects to do is to keep on moving at the same speed. It takes a force to change the motion.

Figure 8 The natural thing is for moving objects to keep on moving in the same way.

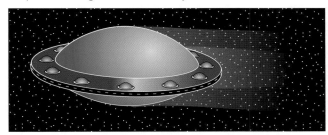

Figure 9 Air resistance and friction provide forces that resist motion. So sometimes we make the mistake of thinking that moving objects always slow down and stop. Now that we can picture spacecraft moving where there is no air to slow them down, it's easier for us to see that steady motion IS what happens naturally.

Figure 10 Newton also said that the everyday force that makes apples fall off trees is the SAME kind of force as the force that keeps the Moon in orbit around the Earth and keeps the planets in orbit around the Sun. It is the force of gravity.

Stories of the Solar System

In the past, many people believed that the Earth was at the centre of everything – the centre of the Universe. This idea is called the **geocentric Universe**.

People studied the planets. A monk called **Copernicus** suggested that the planets go round the Sun and not round the Earth. It matched what people could see. They discovered that we go round the Sun, just like the other planets. The idea that the Sun is at the centre of the Solar System is called the **heliocentric** idea.

The planets are the Sun's natural **satellites**. Most of the planets have their own smaller satellites, called moons.

We use a capital M only for our Moon because it is close to us and more important to us than all the other moons.

Artificial satellites

We can launch artificial satellites into orbit round the Earth. We can use them to look for energy resources or for pollution, or to find our way around.

The orbits of TV satellites are timed to match the orbit of the Earth. They stay in the same place above the Earth. They are called geostationary satellites.

Figure 11 Some satellite cameras use 'invisible light', such as infra red light. Weather satellites, for example, often make their pictures using infra red.

Figure 12 You may have a receiver of satellite signals on the side of your house. The signals travel between satellite and ground using radio waves which are another form of 'invisible light'.

Revision

1 What was 'revolutionary' about the ideas of Copernicus, Galileo and Newton?

2 On a full page, make a concept map. Use the words gravity and orbit as your central starting words. Show how all of the other words from the Key Words list from this chapter are linked to the two starter words.

Questions

1 a) Why can the forces acting on a parachutist on the Moon never become balanced during the fall?

b) Why wouldn't a helicopter work on the Moon?

2 a) In space science, what is the unit of mass?

b) In space science, what is the unit of weight?

c) Name a difference, apart from their units, between mass and weight.

3 Describe two ways to lose weight.

4 Think about some moving objects such as a bag sliding across the floor, a rolling ball, a skater and a spacecraft.

a) What does your 'common sense' tell you about what is more natural – steady motion or slowing down and stopping?

b) Do you think that the ideas of Galileo and Newton agree or disagree with your 'common sense'?

c) Is 'common sense' always a reliable way of understanding how the world behaves?

5 a) Why doesn't a satellite in orbit around the Earth slow down?

b) In what way is the satellite's motion changing all the time?

6 a) What is the difference between the geocentric idea and the heliocentric idea of the Solar System?

b) Which idea do you prefer?

7 Explain why satellite pictures are useful to:

a) fishing boat crews

b) the organiser of your school Summer Fair.

8.4 Speeding up

Key Words

average speed	**thrust**
metres per second	**drag**
instantaneous speed	**distance–time graph**
precision	**streamlines**
gradient	**turbulence**
lift	

Every 0.01 second counts

Athletics events are timed with high **precision**. The time is measured to the nearest hundredth of a second. A hundredth of a second is written as 0.01 seconds, or just 0.01 s.

A sprinter can travel 10 centimetres in that time.

An athlete's **average speed** for a race is found from the total distance divided by the total time they take.

$$\text{Average speed} = \frac{\text{total distance}}{\text{total time}}$$

Always start a calculation by writing down the formula you are using.

If the total distance is 10 000 m and the total time is 29 minutes, 31.78 seconds (or 1771.78 seconds), then:

$$\text{average speed} = \frac{10\,000}{1771.78}$$

Write the formula again, putting the numbers in place of their names.
Then use a calculator to do the arithmetic. And don't forget to write the name of the unit as well as the number.

average speed = 5.64 metres per second

The athlete doesn't run at exactly 5.64 **metres per second** for the whole race. Speed can change from one instant to the next. The speed at one particular instant is called **instantaneous speed**.

Figure 1   The athletes in this race were timed to the nearest hundredth of a second. An athlete has only one average speed for a whole race, but has lots of different instantaneous speeds

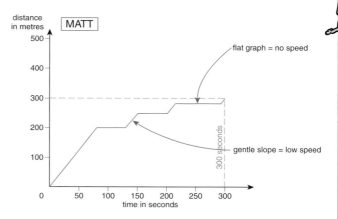

MATT

flat graph = no speed

gentle slope = low speed

300 seconds

High Street travellers

Matt, Vicky, Ellie and Ali don't know each other, but they all travel along Milford High Street at about the same time on a busy Saturday afternoon.

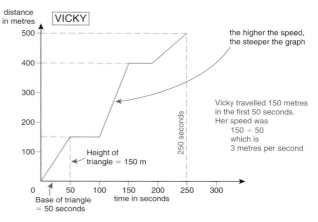

VICKY

the higher the speed, the steeper the graph

Height of triangle = 150 m

Base of triangle = 50 seconds

250 seconds

Vicky travelled 150 metres in the first 50 seconds. Her speed was
150 ÷ 50
which is
3 metres per second

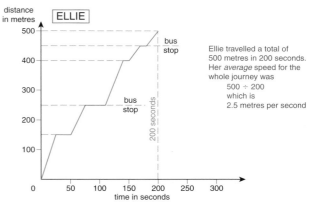

ELLIE

bus stop

bus stop

200 seconds

Ellie travelled a total of 500 metres in 200 seconds. Her *average* speed for the whole journey was
500 ÷ 200
which is
2.5 metres per second

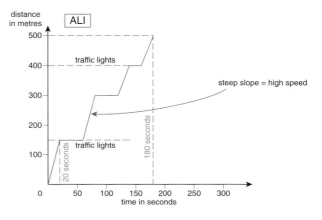

ALI

traffic lights

traffic lights

steep slope = high speed

20 seconds

180 seconds

Figure 2 Distance–time graphs for the four High Street travellers

> We tell the stories of journeys, with distance–time graphs.

Look at the graphs for the High Street travellers. Whenever they stop, the distances don't change and the graphs become level lines. The faster they go, the steeper the slopes of the graphs.

We can use the graphs to work out average speeds for their *complete* journeys. The graphs tell us the total distance travelled and the total time, and we divide these.

We can also work out the speed for *parts* of the journeys, from the steepness or **gradient** of the graphs.

Where the graph is flat there isn't any steepness so the gradient is zero and this matches the speed.

Where the graph is steep, the speed is large. We can work the speed out by using the line of the graph as part of a triangle. You can see this on Vicky's graph. We can measure the height of the triangle to find out distance and we can measure the base of the triangle to find out the matching time. We divide the height (distance) by base (time) for the first part of Vicky's journey.

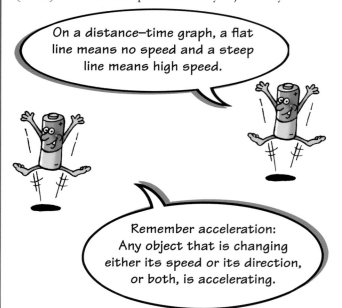

> On a distance–time graph, a flat line means no speed and a steep line means high speed.

> Remember acceleration: Any object that is changing either its speed or its direction, or both, is accelerating.

Force and motion in flight

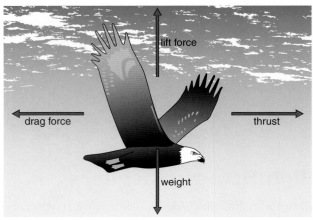

Figure 3 The vertical forces are weight and lift. They are the same size so they are balanced. The horizontal forces are thrust and drag. They are also equal to each other. They are balanced forces. The bird flies at a steady speed, without acceleration or deceleration.

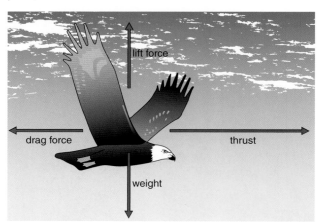

Figure 4 The vertical forces are in balance, but the horizontal forces are not. The bird accelerates forwards.

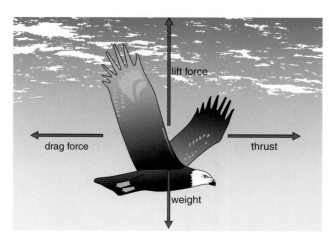

Figure 5 Now the vertical forces are not balanced. The bird accelerates upwards. It has to work hard to create a strong force of lift to do this.

Streamlines and turbulence

Figure 6 Car companies put their car designs into wind tunnels and blast air at the cars. This car has tapes fixed to it to show which way the air is moving at different places. Sometimes they put smoke into the air so that they can see the flow of air and smoke across the surface of the car. The lines of smoke show the air's streamlines. If the streamlines are smooth, then drag forces are not too big. We might say that the car is well streamlined. If the streamlines break up into chaotic swirls, the drag forces become a lot bigger. This breaking up of streamlines is called turbulence. Cars are designed to stop turbulence happening too much.

The faster a car travels, the faster it has to push air out of the way. This makes more air resistance, so the car and its engine have to do more work to overcome it. This means that the car uses more fuel, which costs more and produces more pollution. Car makers try to design cars so that the force of air resistance, or drag, is as low as possible.

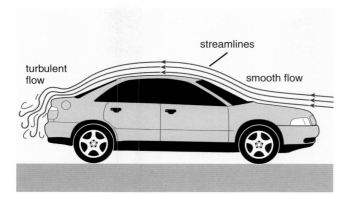

Figure 7 The difference between smooth and turbulent flow.

Air resistance and particles

Figure 8 An airliner goes very fast so it has to push air out of the way *very* quickly. It collides with the particles of the air. These particles might not be very big, but there are a lot of them and the plane hits them hard. The particles of the plane's metal hit the particles of air. The result of all these particle crashes is that particles in the plane's metal are made to vibrate with more energy. The metal gets hotter.

Hodder Science Summary Book

Revision

1 What's the difference between:

- average speed and instantaneous speed
- metres per second and metres
- lift and thrust
- distance–time graph and gradient
- streamlines and turbulence?

2 Speed cyclists try to make their bodies as streamlined as possible. How do they do this and why is it important?

Questions

1 Sort the units given below into three lists – one for units of distance, one for units of time, and one for units of speed.

metres   seconds   hours

kilometres per hour   centimetre

metres per second   kilometres   miles

milliseconds   miles per hour

2 a) Why doesn't a spacecraft need a thrust force to keep going at steady speed?

b) What happens when a thrust force acts on a spacecraft?

3 Write these times in decimal form:

a) one hundredth of a second

b) two hundredths of a second

c) a tenth of a second.

4 For the sprinter running 10 cm in 0.01s, what is their speed in:

a) centimetres per second?

b) metres per second?

5 a) What is an athlete's speed at the instant that the starting gun goes off?

b) Two seconds before the athlete finishes, is the instantaneous speed likely to be bigger or smaller than her average speed for the whole race?

6 a) How big is the gradient of a distance–time graph for a traveller who is not moving?

b) What happens as the traveller moves faster and faster?

7 a) Use information from the graphs in Figure 2 to work out the average speeds for Matt, Vicky and Ali.

b) How far down the street had Ali gone when the car stopped to let his brother out? How long did the car stop for?

c) Draw a map of the street and show the positions of the traffic lights and Ellie's bus stops. Show the distances of these from the start of the street.

8 What happens to a bird when

a) drag is bigger than thrust?

b) thrust is bigger than drag?

9 a) Why does a plane experience *much* more drag force than a person riding a bike?

b) What is the cause of drag?

10 a) If a car is 'streamlined', what does this mean?

b) What is turbulence? Why is it often a problem?

8.5 Forces in action

Key Words

area	compressible
pressure	hydraulic
inverse	moment
relationship	pivot
pascal	

There is an inverse relationship between pressure and area. When one gets bigger, the other gets smaller (as long as the force stays the same).

Elephant pressure

Figure 1

The large feet of an elephant spread its weight over a large area so that the big weight doesn't have too much effect on the ground below. The pressure is not too big. But sometimes, large **pressure** is a good thing. Pointed tusks are very convenient for digging for food or water. The small **area** of the points produces a large pressure for the same force.

Figure 2 A knife uses the small area of its sharp edge to create a large pressure

Your personal pressure

The force you exert on the floor is your weight. But the pressure you exert on the floor depends on your weight and also on the area of your shoe or foot that is in contact with the ground. You can change the area of contact by standing on your toes or by standing on the edges of your shoes.

In all cases we can work out the pressure from the size of the force and the area of contact.

$$\text{Pressure} = \frac{\text{Force}}{\text{Area}}$$

That is, pressure is force divided by area.

The **pascal**, or Pa for short, is the international unit of pressure. It is equivalent to a force of 1 newton acting on an area of 1 square metre.

Atmospheric pressure

We all live at the bottom of a sea of air – the Earth's atmosphere. The air presses on our bodies. It exerts an atmospheric pressure.

Figure 3 We are used to 100 000 pascal of atmospheric pressure acting on our skin. Our bodies on the insides of our skin push out to balance the air pressure. In space there is no air. Our bodies would explode if we didn't wear special pressurised space suits

Water pressure

Air exerts pressure on all of the skin of our bodies. So does water when we go below the water's surface. Every 11 metres of depth of water adds pressure that is equal to the pressure of the whole of the atmosphere.

Figure 4 The deeper this diver goes, the greater will be the pressure on her.

Working under pressure

We can calculate the pressure exerted by the firefighter in Figure 5 as follows:

Weight of firefighter	=	800 newtons
Area of feet in contact with roof when standing	=	0.01 square metres
Area when on crawling board	=	1 square metre
Pressure on roof when standing	=	force/area
	=	800/0.01
	=	80 000 pascal
Pressure on roof when on crawling board	=	force/area = 800/1
	=	800 pascal

Figure 5 The crawling board reduces the pressure of the firefighter by spreading out his weight

Remember: pressure is force divided by area.

Hydraulics

Pressure applied to liquids does not reduce their volume. They are **incompressible**. So when we apply extra pressure to a liquid it pushes out with the same extra pressure everywhere on its container. We use this in **hydraulic** machinery.

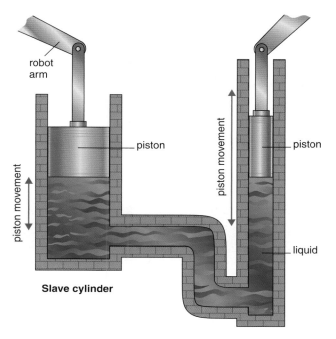

Slave cylinder

Master cylinder

Figure 6   A hydraulic master cylinder has a master piston with a small area. The master piston is pushed so pressure acts on the liquid. The liquid presses on the slave piston in the slave cylinder. The liquid 'transmits' the pressure from one piston to the other. The pressure on the slave piston is the same as the pressure provided by the master cylinder. But the same pressure acting over a bigger area provides a bigger force. Using hydraulics in this way we can use a small force to create a big one

Using a machine to provide a bigger force from a smaller one is called force multiplication.

Gases

Pressure applied to gases reduces their volume. They are **compressible**, unlike liquids.

Figure 7   The compressibility, or sponginess, of gas in the tyres gives a less bumpy ride on a bike

In a gas, the particles are a long way apart and it's not too hard to push them closer together. In a liquid, it is very hard to push particles much closer together. So the particle idea can explain the different behaviour of gases and liquids under pressure.

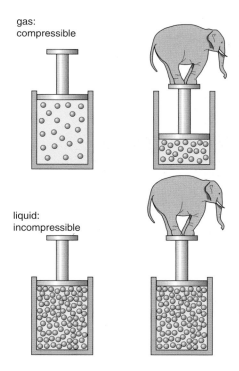

Figure 8   A gas under pressure (top) and a liquid under pressure (bottom)

163

Forces at play

In playgrounds, children play with the force of gravity and with the turning effects of forces.

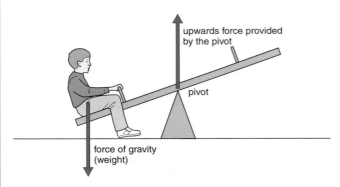

Figure 9 On a see-saw, the force of gravity can produce a turning effect. You can see that the upward force and the downward force are the same size, but they do not pass through the same point, so they are not balanced

Figure 10 The force of gravity acting on a second person can also produce a turning effect

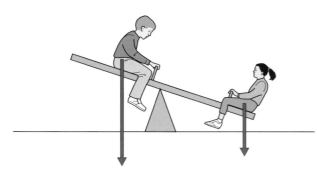

Figure 11 A smaller person can have a bigger turning effect than a big one by sitting far enough from the see-saw pivot

Turning effect = force × distance of force from pivot

Another name for the turning effect of a force is the **moment** of the force. Forces are measured in newtons and distances are measured in metres. So turning effects or moments are measured in newton metres.

A force that has a clockwise turning effect has a clockwise moment. A see-saw will be balanced when the total of the clockwise moments is the same as the total of the anti-clockwise moments. That is, for balance:

total clockwise moments = total anticlockwise moments

This is called the principle of moments.

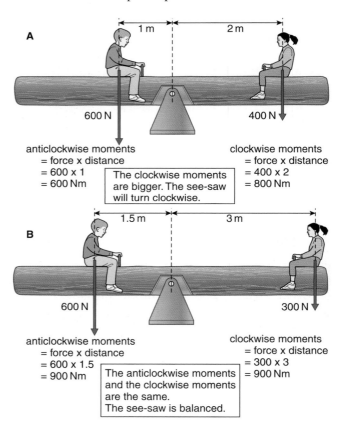

Figure 12

Body balance

We can use the principle of moments to help us to understand a wide range of situations, including hazardous situations.

Turning effect not wanted!

Turning effect wanted.

Figure 14 This tightrope walker is using a pole to help make smooth and well-controlled adjustments to the moments acting. The clockwise moments must equal the anticlockwise moments so that there is no turning effect

Figure 13 The unbalanced force of gravity is giving the gymnast an anti-clockwise moment. Her hands on the bar act as the pivot. The principle of moments is not being satisfied. Total clockwise moments are not equal to total anticlockwise moments. So the gymnast experiences a turning (rotational) acceleration

Hodder Science Summary Book

Revision

Use the Key Words on page 161 to make your own word puzzle. Make up clues for your puzzle. If possible, give your puzzle to somebody else to see if they can complete it.

Questions

1 When you are standing up, you usually have your feet flat on the floor. What can you do to increase the pressure that you exert on the floor? Use the words weight and area in your answer.

2 a) What is an inverse relationship?

   b) Name two variables that have an inverse relationship.

3 Use the words area and pressure to explain how a knife can cut through cheese.

4 Calculate the pressure exerted by a 600 newton person standing on the floor. The area of the bottom of their shoes, touching the floor, is 0.01 square metres.

5 In a hydraulic system, what design feature makes the force exerted by the slave piston bigger than the force exerted on the master piston?

6 Some running shoes have big air bubbles in the heels. Particles in a gas, like air, are far apart. Particles in a liquid are very close together. How does this explain why the shoe designers don't use bubbles of liquid in the heels of their shoes?

7 a) Make a table to show the moment of a force of 100 newtons when it acts 1 metre, 2 metres, 3 metres, 4 metres and 5 metres from a pivot.

   b) Add another line or column to your table to show the distances that a 50 newton force must be from the pivot to produce balance for each position of the 100 newton force.

8 For a tightrope walker, where is the pivot?

9 The tightrope walker in Figure 14 is in a hazardous situation.

   a) What is the main risk?

   b) How does the tightrope walker reduce the risk?

   c) Do you think that the tightrope walker is taking an 'acceptable' risk?

Light and sound

9.1 Light

Key Words

source	output variable
ray	refraction
colour	angle of incidence
texture	normal
image	spectrum
scattering	absorb
angle	filter
angle of	disperse
reflection	white light
input variable	reflect

Figure 1 The sun is a source of light

Sources of light

The Sun is a **source** of light, and so are light bulbs, candles and camera flashguns. Their light travels very quickly to reach our eyes.

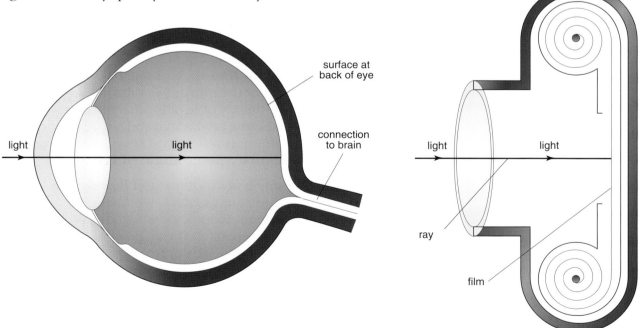

Figure 2 In an eye and a camera, light travels through a lens to a surface at the back. Inside the camera, the pattern on the film matches the light that shines on to it. It makes a photograph. Light also produces changes on the surface at the back of your eyeball. The changes cause the start of impulses in the nerves that are connected to your brain, and that is how you see

Reflections

Figure 3   This is a cave painting in Lascaux in France. It was painted 17 000 years ago. For thousands of years the painting was in darkness. Then some people went into the cave with lamps. The light from their lamps reached the surfaces and the surfaces reflected the light. Some of the reflected light reached these people's eyes

Different surfaces **reflect** the light in different ways. In the caves in Figure 3 there were shiny pools of water on the floor. The water surfaces were smooth, like mirrors. There were the rough surfaces of the rock. The texture of a surface – whether it is rough or smooth – affects how it reflects light. It affects how it looks to us.

White surfaces reflect a lot of the light. Black surfaces reflect very little light. Coloured surfaces are choosy. They only reflect some kinds of light.

It's much easier to think about how light is reflected if we think about just a single ray at a time.

Seeing ourselves

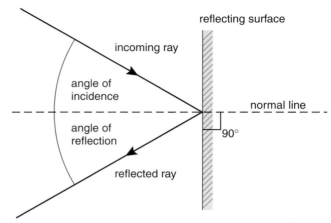

Figure 4   A **ray** is a pathway of light, like a VERY narrow beam

A **normal line** sticks straight out at 90° to the surface of the mirror. We draw it at the point where the ray of light is reflected. Then we can measure the angles that the ray makes before and after it is reflected. These are the **angle of incidence** and the **angle of reflection**.

The angle of incidence and the angle of reflection are variables. We can do an experiment to look for a relationship between the two variables. The angle of incidence is the input variable. We control its size. Every time we measure the angle of incidence, we then also measure the angle of reflection. The angle of reflection is the output variable.

The light we see is the light that the surfaces reflect.

Angle of incidence	Angle of reflection
14°	14°
26°	25°
38°	39°

Table 1 Some results of measurement of angles of incidence and reflection

There is a simple relationship between the two variables. The angle of incidence and the angle of reflection are always the same. This discovery is called the **law of reflection**.

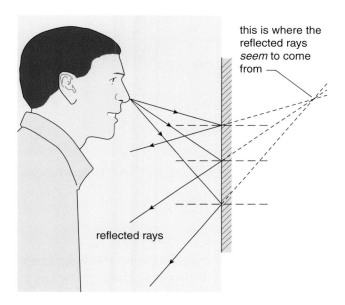

Figure 5 We can draw just a few rays spreading from a point on a face. The rays all obey the law of reflection. The rays seem to be coming from somewhere inside the mirror – that is where we see the image

Every ray *obeys* the law of reflection.

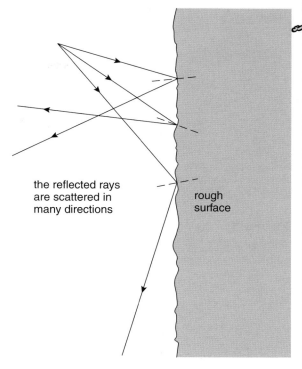

Figure 6 Mirrors have very smooth surfaces. Rough surfaces can also reflect light but they don't produce clear images. The bumps on the surface reflect the light in different directions. Reflection like this is called **scattering** of the light

Light changing direction

Refraction happens at surfaces (such as water and glass surfaces) and can change the direction of the light.

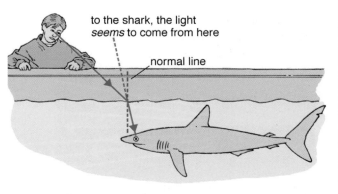

Figure 7 How to confuse a shark! To the shark's eye, the place where the light seems to come from is not where it actually comes from

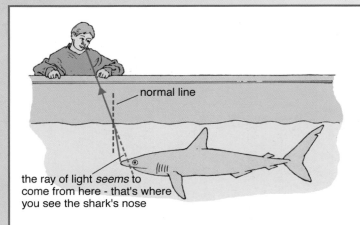

Figure 8 How to confuse a human! When a person looks through a water surface at a shark, the place a ray seems to come from is not where it actually comes from

Glass surfaces **refract** light. To see just how much a ray is bent we can draw a normal line, and then measure the incident angle and the refracted angle.

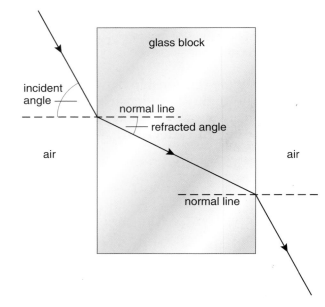

Figure 9 Measuring the incident and refracted angles in glass

Movies

Very old films are in black and white. Each frame of the film produces shadows on the screen. Black areas of the frame absorb the light and make dark shadows.

Transparent areas of the frame let the light from the projector shine through to the screen. Grey areas of the frame absorb some of the light.

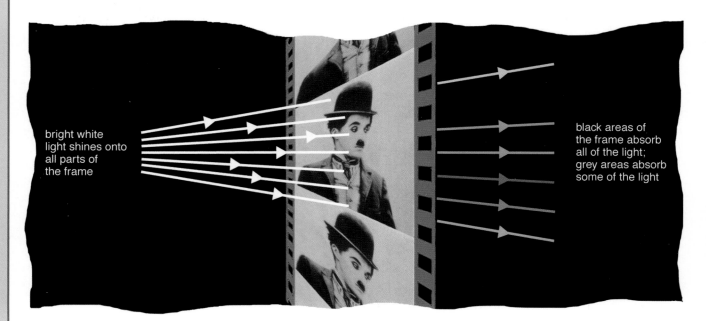

Figure 10 How a black and white film works

For a colour movie, a red area of the frame lets red light shine through. Coloured areas of the frame act as **filters**. They absorb some colours of light but let other colours travel on through.

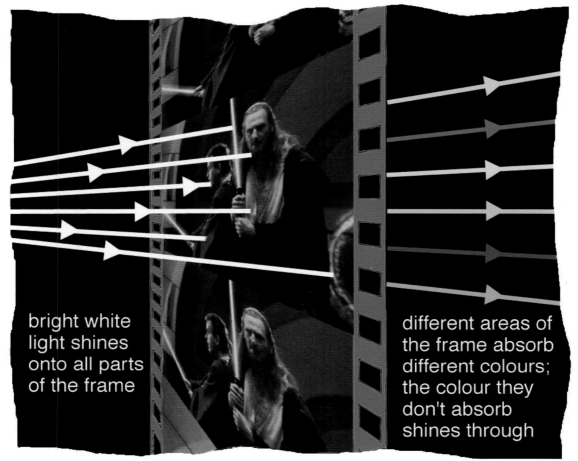

bright white light shines onto all parts of the frame

different areas of the frame absorb different colours; the colour they don't absorb shines through

Figure 11   How a colour film works

White light seems to be a mixture of all colours. We can try out this idea by shining a thin beam of white light through a prism. What we see is a rainbow of colour, called a spectrum. We say that the prism has **dispersed** the light.

Revision

1   Use these words to start a concept map. Add small sketch diagrams to show what the words mean.

> **source   ray   reflection
> refraction   absorption**

2   Add these words to your concept map:

> **colour   texture   image   scattering
> angle of incidence   angle of reflection
> normal   spectrum   filter   dispersion
> white light**

Figure 12   A prism dispersing lights

Hodder Science Summary Book

1 a) Where is the light coming from for you to see this book?

b) Would you be able to see the book if there were no sources of light shining on to it (such as in a cave)?

c) What does the surface of the book do to the light?

2 Make careful sketches to show a ray of light:

a) being reflected by a mirror

b) being refracted as it goes from air to glass.

3 Why can't you see your reflection in a rough surface?

4 a) Explain how light makes your hand visible to you.

b) The same light shines on your hand and on a red book cover. What happens to make the surfaces look different?

5 a) Run your fingers across this page and the cover of the book. Describe all the differences you can feel and see between the two surfaces.

b) Explain how reflection of light makes the page and the cover look different.

6 a) What is the name of the law that rays obey when they are reflected?

b) Write down the law.

7 Use your knowledge of refraction to explain why the world looks distorted when you look through a glass of water. You could use drawings to help your explanation.

8 White light from a projector shines onto a frame of film. Describe the light that shines through areas of the film that are

a) completely clear or transparent

b) solid black

c) grey

d) red

e) blue

f) green.

9 A prism separates white light into colours.

a) What is this process called?

b) What kind of light would you see if you could mix the colours up again?

10 Coloured objects often look strange when you see them under a coloured light. What colour would these snooker balls seem to be?

a) a red ball in red light

b) a red ball in blue light

c) a blue ball in red light

d) a green ball in white light

e) a white ball in green light.

9.2 Sound and music

Key Words

eardrum	microphone
vibration	oscilloscope
frequency	ultrasound
loudness	vacuum
pitch	kilohertz
amplitude	decibel
wave	hertz

The travelling vibrations are called waves.

Travelling vibrations

The crash of a drumstick makes the drumskin vibrate. That makes the air around it vibrate. The **vibration** spreads through the air. Vibrations travel quickly – about one kilometre every three seconds.

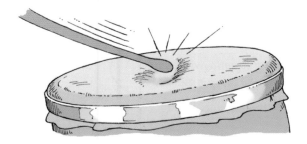

Figure 1   A drum vibrating

The vibrations of the air make your **eardrum** vibrate. Your eardrum makes some tiny bones in your ear vibrate. The bones pass the vibrations on to a liquid deeper inside your ear. There are tiny hairs in the liquid. They vibrate too, and they make tiny electric bursts in your nerves. Your brain can understand these electric bursts. It calls them sound.

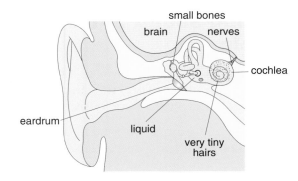

Figure 2   A cross section through the ear

Different sounds

You usually use the voicebox in your throat to speak. You make your voicebox vibrate in different ways, so that you can make different sounds. You also use your mouth to make different patterns of sound.

Figure 3   a) Gentle talk – lungs, voicebox, tongue and lips are all busy. They make louder and quieter sounds. They make high and low notes.
b) Singing out loud – now your voicebox is really working hard. The voicebox needs to put more energy into vibrations to make loud sounds

Loudness and amplitude

A guitar string vibrates to make sound. The **amplitude** of a vibration is the distance the string moves away from its resting position. When the amplitude of vibration increases, the loudness of the sound also increases.

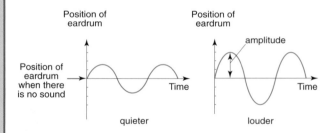

Figure 4 We can use graphs like these to show vibrations. They show how the position of the centre of a vibrating object, like an eardrum, changes as time goes by.

Pitch and frequency

Guitars and people's voices can make high **pitch** sounds and low pitch sounds.

The **frequency** of a source of sound is the number of vibrations it makes in every second. Guitar strings usually vibrate with fairly high frequency, hundreds of times each second. All you can see is a blur. High frequency vibrations make high pitch notes.

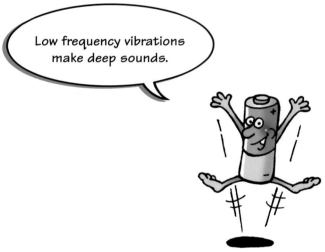

We measure frequency in **hertz**, or Hz for short. 1 Hz is one vibration per second.

Making sound patterns visible

Sound waves cause vibrations in a microphone. The microphone converts the vibrations into a matching pattern of electric current.

We can connect a microphone to an **oscilloscope**. It turns the electric current from the microphone into patterns we can see. This makes it easier to compare different sounds.

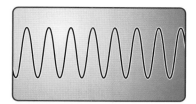
a continuous
steady note

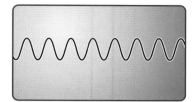
a quiet note

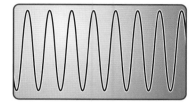
a louder note

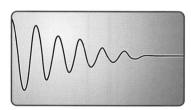
a note that
quickly fades

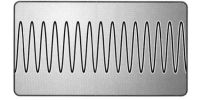
a note with higher
frequency

Figure 5   Sound shapes as they appear on the screen
of an oscilloscope

Comparing light and sound

Sound and light spread out from sources. There
are other similarities and differences between
light and sound.

Sound travels much more slowly than light –
almost a million times more slowly in air. The
speed of sound in air is about 330 metres per
second.

Sound can travel through materials that light
cannot penetrate. In fact sounds travel more
easily, and faster, in solids and liquids than they
do in gases like air.

> Sound can travel through
> you – as you can tell every
> time your stomach rumbles.

Sound needs a substance to travel through. It
cannot travel through a vacuum, but light can.

Both light and sound reflect off surfaces.

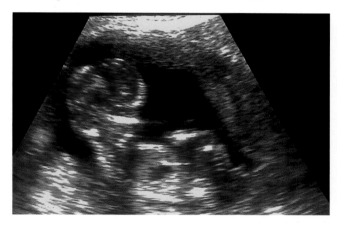

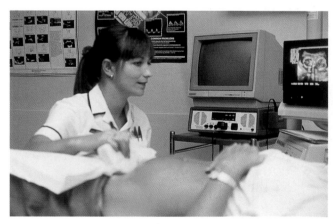

Figure 6   Ultrasound reflections from inside a human
body can be used to produce images of unborn babies.
Ultrasound is very high frequency sound – too high for
any human to hear. For scanning, the frequency could be
as high as 3.5 megahertz. (1 megahertz is 1 million hertz,
or 1 million vibrations every second)

Ears – what can go wrong?

Look again at Figure 2 on page 173.

- A build-up of ear wax in the outer ear can cause temporary reduction in hearing sensitivity.

- Sound arriving at the eardrum makes it vibrate. The eardrum is a circle of stretched skin that can be burst by sudden loud noises such as explosions.

- The small bones transmit the vibrations from the eardrum towards the inner ear. They are very small and delicate.

- The cochlea is in the inner ear. It is a coiled tube filled with liquid. Small hairs on the cochlea move in time to incoming vibrations. They create electrical signals that travel into the brain, so that we can hear. The hairs can be damaged by loud sounds, such as the sounds from high-power music speakers or industrial machinery. The damage is permanent. There is no way to repair the tiny hairs.

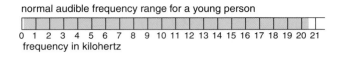

normal audible frequency range for a young person

frequency in kilohertz

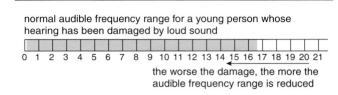

normal audible frequency range for a young person whose hearing has been damaged by loud sound

the worse the damage, the more the audible frequency range is reduced

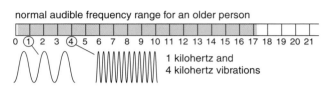

normal audible frequency range for an older person

1 kilohertz and 4 kilohertz vibrations

Figure 7 Some audible frequency ranges measured in **kilohertz**. A kilohertz is a thousand hertz. Children have the biggest audible frequency range. As you get older you lose some of your ability to hear high frequencies

Questions

1 If you watch a film on TV, where on the TV is the source of the sound?

2 A clap of thunder and a flash of lightning come from the same place. You usually see the lightning before you hear the thunder. Why?

3 The Sun makes a lot of vibrations. Why can't we hear the Sun?

4 Put your ear to the desk. Get your partner to scratch the desk. Does sound travel better through air or wood?

5 What does a guitar player have to do to play notes of different pitch?

6 Put these words into pairs that go together:

microphone   amplitude   pitch
frequency   oscilloscope   loudness

7 What evidence is there that:

a) light can travel through a vacuum?

b) sound can travel through solids and liquids?

8 What difference could you hear between a 60 dB sound and a 40 dB sound?

9 Loud sounds are a health hazard.

a) What damage can they do?

b) In what situations are people exposed to loud sounds?

c) What safety precautions reduce the risk of damage?

10 What do each of these units measure:
a) hertz?
b) kilohertz?
c) decibel?

Revision

What's the difference between:

- your eardrums and a musical drum

- a vibration and a wave

- loudness and pitch

- amplitude and frequency

- a microphone and an oscilloscope

- sound and ultrasound

- a vacuum, a gas and a solid

- a hertz, a kilohertz and a decibel?

Periodic table of the elements

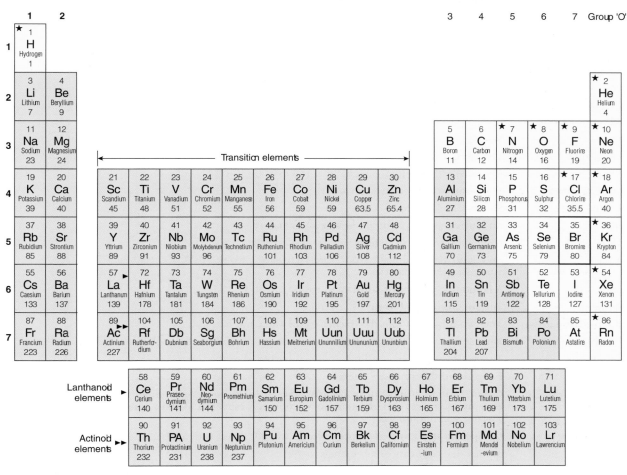

	1	2												3	4	5	6	7	Group 'O'
1	★ 1 **H** Hydrogen 1																		★ 2 **He** Helium 4
2	3 **Li** Lithium 7	4 **Be** Beryllium 9												5 **B** Boron 11	6 **C** Carbon 12	★ 7 **N** Nitrogen 14	★ 8 **O** Oxygen 16	★ 9 **F** Fluorine 19	★ 10 **Ne** Neon 20
3	11 **Na** Sodium 23	12 **Mg** Magnesium 24				Transition elements								13 **Al** Aluminium 27	14 **Si** Silicon 28	15 **P** Phosphorus 31	16 **S** Sulphur 32	★ 17 **Cl** Chlorine 35.5	★ 18 **Ar** Argon 40
4	19 **K** Potassium 39	20 **Ca** Calcium 40	21 **Sc** Scandium 45	22 **Ti** Titanium 48	23 **V** Vanadium 51	24 **Cr** Chromium 52	25 **Mn** Manganese 55	26 **Fe** Iron 56	27 **Co** Cobalt 59	28 **Ni** Nickel 59	29 **Cu** Copper 63.5	30 **Zn** Zinc 65.4	31 **Ga** Gallium 70	32 **Ge** Germanium 73	33 **As** Arsenic 75	34 **Se** Selenium 79	35 **Br** Bromine 80	★ 36 **Kr** Krypton 84
5	37 **Rb** Rubidium 85	38 **Sr** Strontium 88	39 **Y** Yttrium 89	40 **Zr** Zirconium 91	41 **Nb** Niobium 93	42 **Mo** Molybdenum 96	43 **Tc** Technetium	44 **Ru** Ruthenium 101	45 **Rh** Rhodium 103	46 **Pd** Palladium 106	47 **Ag** Silver 108	48 **Cd** Cadmium 112	49 **In** Indium 115	50 **Sn** Tin 119	51 **Sb** Antimony 122	52 **Te** Tellurium 128	53 **I** Iodine 127	★ 54 **Xe** Xenon 131
6	55 **Cs** Caesium 133	56 **Ba** Barium 137	57 ► **La** Lanthanum 139	72 **Hf** Hafnium 178	73 **Ta** Tantalum 181	74 **W** Tungsten 184	75 **Re** Rhenium 186	76 **Os** Osmium 190	77 **Ir** Iridium 192	78 **Pt** Platinum 195	79 **Au** Gold 197	80 **Hg** Mercury 201	81 **Tl** Thallium 204	82 **Pb** Lead 207	83 **Bi** Bismuth	84 **Po** Polonium	85 **At** Astatine	★ 86 **Rn** Radon
7	87 **Fr** Francium 223	88 **Ra** Radium 226	89 ►► **Ac** Actinium 227	104 **Rf** Rutherfo-dium	105 **Db** Dubnium	106 **Sg** Seaborgium	107 **Bh** Bohrium	108 **Hs** Hassium	109 **Mt** Meitnerium	110 **Uun** Ununnilium	111 **Uuu** Unununium	112 **Uub** Ununbium						

Lanthanoid elements ►

58 **Ce** Cerium 140	59 **Pr** Praseo-dymium 141	60 **Nd** Neo-dymium 144	61 **Pm** Promethium	62 **Sm** Samarium 150	63 **Eu** Europium 152	64 **Gd** Gadolinium 157	65 **Tb** Terbium 159	66 **Dy** Dysprosium 163	67 **Ho** Holmium 165	68 **Er** Erbium 167	69 **Tm** Thulium 169	70 **Yb** Ytterbium 173	71 **Lu** Lutetium 175

Actinoid elements ►►

90 **Th** Thorium 232	91 **PA** Protactinium 231	92 **U** Uranium 238	93 **Np** Neptunium 237	94 **Pu** Plutonium	95 **Am** Americium	96 **Cm** Curium	97 **Bk** Berkelium	98 **Cf** Californium	99 **Es** Einstein-ium	100 **Fm** Fermium	101 **Md** Mendel-evium	102 **No** Nobelium	103 **Lr** Lawrencium

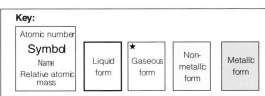

Key:

Atomic number
Symbol
Name
Relative atomic mass

| Liquid form | ★ Gaseous form | Non-metallic form | Metallic form |

Glossary

Glossary

Glossary

Glossary

Glossary